Confou

An expression of gratitude
from a member of the first of many generations
to have their Christian faith formed
by the writing and teaching of C.S. Lewis.

Herbert O'Driscoll

Confound Them!

Diabolical Plans for the Church

Herbert O'Driscoll

Anglican Book Centre
Toronto, Canada

Published
2000 by
Anglican Book Centre
600 Jarvis Street
Toronto, Ontario
M4Y 2J6

Picture acknowledgement: "The Building of the Tower of Babel." Bodleian Library, Oxford.

Canadian Cataloguing in Publication Data
O'Driscoll, Herbert, 1928-
Confound them! : diabolical plans for the church

ISBN 1-55126-318-1

1. Anglican Communion — Doctrines. 2. Church renewal — Anglican Communion.
I. Title.

BX5005.O37 2000 283 C00-931892-5

Contents

Wherever God erects a house of prayer,
The Devil always builds a chapel there;
And 'twill be found upon examination,
The latter has the largest congregation.

Daniel Defoe (1661–1731)

A Word to the Reader

The recent and unexpected death of my Uncle Richard has left me with an extraordinary and, I think, extremely significant legacy. For a number of years he has been the rector of a large downtown church where he has enabled the emergence of a number of ministry initiatives, particularly in the more run-down areas of the city. I can only assume that his insistence on continuing to shoulder the stresses of this work well into his upper sixties brought about the heart condition that eventually ended his life.

When his estate was distributed by the family lawyer, a long-time friend, I was surprised to find that my uncle, a lifelong confirmed bachelor, had left me a very welcome legacy of some ten thousand dollars, a very fine up to date library, and a bundle of letters.

Human nature being what it is, I took less time to spend the ten thousand dollars than to get around to examining the letters. Recently I turned to them, spilling them out of the large brown envelope, prepared to be thoroughly bored by my allotted task. Suffice it to say that my boredom dissipated quickly as I read the accompanying letter from my uncle, written a few months before his death and addressed to me. I quote only the relevant parts of it.

> Now I come to the real reason why I have involved you in my affairs. I have appreciated our friendship over the years, watching you grow into a man of deep Christian faith and practice. Because of this I have decided that

you are the one among my many friends and acquaintances with whom I can responsibly share the strange way in which I came to be in possession of the letters you are about to read.

While I had not given thought to retirement until the onset of this illness, I realize now that in recent months I must have been subconsciously aware that my ministry was approaching its limits. For whatever reason, conscious or unconscious, I began to go through the many file drawers that are a constant presence in church offices. Most held only the expected files of ancient stewardship campaigns, visitation rosters, church bulletins, and the like.

However, in one drawer, right at the back, I came across the letters you now have in your possession. Thinking them to be of no more interest than the rest of what I had discovered, I nearly deposited them in the waste baskets I was filling with increasing satisfaction. But for some reason I glanced at the first letter, and my interest was caught. As soon as you begin reading, you will understand why I did not cease reading until I had completed every page.

The letters are obviously the work of one hand. For reasons that will become obvious, I hesitate even to use the word *hand* because it assumes human agency. It would seem that someone — dare I say something — in our congregation has been receiving these messages from a source I hesitate to name, but one I fear to be nothing less than demonic. Obviously the tasks assigned to this agent who has infiltrated our institution are for the weakening, even the destruction, of the church you and I love so dearly.

It is obvious, too, that this ghastly undermining of our sacred institution has been going on for at least some decades. It looks to be the source of many of the divisions and stresses that plague us, as well as of those currents in the culture that bear nothing but ill will for the faith and the church.

I have decided to share these letters with you because of your faith and your commitment to the church. I had thought of sending them to our bishop but, good man that he is, he is too much a creature of the Enlightenment to credit the existence of a demonic presence among us.

I cannot direct you as to a course of action. The decision must belong to you and to those whom you enlist as allies in this struggle. To say I am appalled that this affair should emerge from the context of my own ministry is an understatement. Scripture has long told me that it is possible for us to entertain angels unawares. I can only assume now that it is also possible to entertain demons unawares.

I cannot even guess who this agent could be. Far too many people have access to a church office — secretaries, wardens, countless committee members, cleaning staff — the list is endless. All I can do is exhort you to be even more aware of those solemn words addressed by the apostle Peter to the early Christian communities of his own lifetime: "Be sober, be vigilant; because your adversary the devil, as a roaring lion, walketh about, seeking whom he may devour. Whom resist steadfast in the faith."

Such were the contents of my uncle's letter. You can imagine my shock, first at the very thought that we could actually have moving among us such a demonic presence, secondly that the undermining policies have been carried out with such — I may well say — diabolical cleverness.

I have decided to publish the letters. I wish to make as many people as possible aware of this threat to what we hold dear and wish to cherish. If what is presented in these pages is true, then it needs to be known that there probably exists a vast network of such agents doing the will of him who is constantly referred to as the Dark Lord. If this also be true, then it is even more important that we become aware of another and greater host who serve the one whom the Director refers to as the Enemy. Unless I am greatly mistaken, each of these forces actively seeks the involvement of human beings. Each of us chooses whom we will serve.

Inishnee, Connemara
Ireland
Easter 2000

PS. In every case the letters passed on to me by my uncle were headed in the following bureaucratic manner.

Recipient: Local Agent, Level 1
Project: Mainline Chuches, Millennium 3
Sector: Anglican/Episcopal
Sender: Project Director, Level 9

I see no reason to burden the reader with a reiteration of this on each piece of correspondence. However, I share the format to show how barren is the relationship between these demonic agents, devoid of any basis other than mutual self-interest and survival.

Of Individualism

You are to be congratulated on the parlous state of this institution. You must of course realize that much of your work has been made easier by the trends emerging in the society itself. Your work with the church has been a mere sideshow compared with the far larger operation set in motion by our Master in every aspect of Western culture long before the present century. The ramifications of this are so varied and all-pervasive that I hesitate to try even to outline the full scope of our Master's work. However, since you yourself have worked so diligently and with such success among these Christians, I feel you deserve to be shown where your work fits in with the greater plan.

Some of our planners maintain that our real achievement came from the work of the agent assigned to guide the fertile mind of a seventeenth-century Frenchman named René Descartes. Thank hell that we made a decision some thousands of years ago to assign an agent to watch over any unusual brilliance among these humans. Our breakthrough was Descartes' passionate insistence that the norm for human existence was to live as an autonomous individual. In spite of the fact that this was a perfectly valid insight about human existence — after all, the Enemy had himself designed things this way — it took us a mere two hundred years to warp it grandly. Now, human beings in Western culture believe that any mode of existence other than conmplete autonomy is a perversion and a dire threat to their precious individuality.

Oh, the satisfaction of it! The very idea that human beings are surrounded by other possibilities and resources for their development took second place to their existence as individuals. Within recent decades we have succeeded in almost silencing all claims on their loyalty except those of their own personal desires. Family, community, church, nation — to name only some — have all paled into insignificance compared with the wishes of the individual. In fact, we now have these people in such a condition that whenever any communal or societal entity dares to make the slightest claim on them, especially if the community's claim clashes with that of the individual, there is an immediate indignant outcry followed closely by a passionate appeal to what has come to be known as "rights."

This achievement on our part has brought into being at least two other desirable conditions. The first is that the culture in general now assumes that only the individual has rights. These rights are steadily being augmented. Agents assigned to the legal and parliamentary worlds have assisted in this process. Our confident hope is that we can begin to look forward to the weakening and eventual disintegration of their institutions. At this point it will take little effort on our part to bring about conditions sufficiently chaotic that the pendulum of desire will swing — with such delicious irony — from the hegemony of the individual to the iron rule of a single individual!

Meanwhile, another whole section of our forces has been busily engaged in developing the feelings of the individual. Since individualism has become the paramount way of being in the world, then it follows — or can be made to follow — that the feelings of the individual are paramount in human experience. By now, we have succeeded in almost entirely eradicating their memory of Descartes' statement, "Cogito, ergo sum" — which, as you well know from the days you did all your work in Latin, means "I think, therefore I am" — and have substituted the statement, "I feel, therefore I am." As experienced demons, you and I know well that the Enemy requires his creatures to both think and feel, but we have got them all to such a state of emotional and mental excess that balance and moderation are regarded as weakness.

The writing of this letter affords me much pleasure, and I have much more to impart. You will recall that I began by promising to set your own work with the church in the context of the greater plan I have outlined. Believe me, the life and work of the Enemy's official organization has been deeply — dare we hope fatally — affected by these things I have been telling you.

Of Authority

Thank you for your appreciative note in response to my attempt to explain how your work fits in to the bigger picture. From a few things you wrote, I am glad to see that you already are aware of some of the links between the rampant individualism of recent decades and our fervent hope — and the hope of our Master — that, following the failure of so many of our attacks on the church, this at last may be the means of its demise.

As I mentioned in my last letter, not a little satisfaction for us lies in the irony that the Enemy made these creatures as individuals. He even sent his son among them as a most obvious and — I must admit — a rather admirable example of the species. But we have succeeded in taking this gift that the Enemy gave them — their unique and infinitely varied individuality — and nearly making it their nemesis. Our success affords endless satisfaction.

But let us now to the matter of the church. I have read your most recent reports, and I am more than pleased to see how you have succeeded in making even the word *authority* suspect. In fact, you have been brilliantly successful in ensuring that, because the church is an institution, it is regarded by many of its members as inherently hierarchical and, therefore, by its very nature oppressive. It follows that any claims it makes on people to guide or to correct them are vehemently repudiated.

As if this is not a sufficient achievement, you have further succeeded in deluding them that they can retain all the appearance of authority — in such things as scripture and the episcopate — while at the same time rejecting the reality of authority. This is brilliant because it will lull them into the illusion that they still have a church when actually they have little more than a network of clubhouses essentially run by the members and increasingly reflecting their personal tastes in program, liturgy, and personal spirituality.

If this were all, it would be satisfying indeed, but there is more. I have been particularly pleased by our success in polarizing opinion in the church about almost every aspect of its work. The result has been such constant bickering that energy is drained from every congregation — many lay people are discouraged, and many clergy are demoralized. This polarization has been made easy for us by the increasing primacy of personal opinion that feels no obligation to anything other than its own wishes, but it is nonetheless very gratifying.

Most satisfying to me and to others here in the Directorate is the way you have been able to attract to our side — all unknowingly — those very people who believe that authority is essential in the church. Whether they see the sources of authority as primarily scriptural, episcopal, or synodical, their insistence on their own vision of these things ensures the erosion of all authority! They berate the church for its many perceived failures to lead, to resolve irresolvable issues, to evangelize, to engage the young, or to be faithful to tradition (as they define the tradition). The contempt they show for those who do not share their views serves our purpose admirably.

I observe that these people have learned to reject authority in the name of a higher authority that they define as occasion demands. If one is offended by an action of the House of Bishops, or by any church council, or for that matter by the local bishop, one claims to have placed oneself under a higher authority. This may be the Thirty-nine Articles or a particular edition of the *Book of Common Prayer*, a particular translation of scripture or, as ultimate authority, the Holy Spirit. If the objector belongs to a different school of thought in the church, the higher authority appealed to may be called "contemporary reality" or "inclusiveness" or "realism" or "freedom." From the protection of these self-defined and self-chosen authorities one can pour scorn on the contemporary body of Christ as it struggles with the complexities and ambiguities of the present age — realities that this Directorate, through the work of you and many like you, has brought into being.

We now have the glorious prospect of every school of thought in the church regarding every other as the enemy. With little effort we will get them to see that enemies cannot — even should not — coexist, but must go their separate ways in pursuit of their perceived truth. What a wonderful prospect — to break up this contemptible so-called people of God into ever diminishing caravans that become more and more vulnerable to the dangers and pressures we concoct for their journey through the wilderness of the present age.

Of History

While I hate keeping promises, if only because the Enemy invariably does, I am nevertheless writing to you as I said I would, now that I have had an opportunity to peruse some recent memos from other agents in the mainline field. They have only just arrived, but even from the little I have read, I can see that good things are ahead for us. What I have seen so far amounts to a mouth-watering list of opportunities for this church in your part of the project to be made vulnerable to our efforts.

Because we are eternal creatures, not prisoners of time like these humans, you and I regard all of time as our domain. You have also been gifted, as all demons are, with an infinitely long and retentive memory. You must always appreciate the great advantages these attributes give us for our planning and acting. We possess an infinitely long view of what these humans call history.

Thanks to a great deal of brilliant work on our Master's part, late twentieth-century humans regard history with contempt. Some events that to us have occurred only yesterday seem to them to have happened in their remote past, having little or nothing to do with their present lives. Some of their intellectuals actually claim that history no longer exists. This claim had a whole board table of us almost rolling on the floor when it was reported down here.

You will recall without any difficulty the intense enjoyment we all felt when we managed to get the Christian Crusaders of the early Middle Ages to cheerfully turn from their sacramental devotions and slaughter Eastern Christians for no reason other than that these unfortunates looked and dressed and worshipped differently from Europeans. Remember, too, how we all howled with glee at the delightful cruelties Christians inflicted on one another during the episode they came to call their Thirty Years War? We came very near to destroying their so-called Reformation there and then. You will recall that our failure was at that time a great disappointment to us. Since then, we have come to realize the great advantage their rancorous divisions have brought to our Master's work, and how these same divisions have distressed and disappointed the Enemy. Even now, as I write, we have succeeded in creating endless new reasons for division among them, but this is another story for another time.

All these things you know, but I mention them to point you once again to a truth. With very little effort we can convince this present generation that the past is quite irrelevant. Thus we can prevent them from seeing that every present experience somehow reflects the past, which therefore has some valuable lessons to teach them. Let them struggle with the seeming loss of faith in their own day, never once realizing that there has been loss of faith in other ages — or might I say, apparent loss of faith. Let them struggle with what they feel is the apocalyptic nature of their time, without ever realizing that other men and women in other centuries have felt and faced the same sense of apocalypse, and have responded to it creatively and courageously. Let them struggle with a sense of being marginalized by the culture of their time, without ever realizing that the earliest generations of Christian faith were the most marginalized people in the Greco-Roman world.

In a word, we must conspire to make them actually proud of their contemporaneity. Let us make sure that these early third-millennium Christians never refer to the past without applying to it diminishing and dismissive adjectives. As long as they think of Romans and Greeks as ancient Romans and ancient Greeks, as long as they consider all things Jewish to be of the past merely because they are in the Bible, then there is every chance that none of the timeless wisdom of these civilizations will ever make a rich contribution to their abilities to respond to their present experiences.

In all this lies hidden a delicious paradox arising from their human nature. Where we cannot get them to regard their past as irrelevant, we can keep them sentimentally attached to their past. Even more to be desired for our Master's cause, we can get them to preserve their past at all costs, never changing it, never adapting its insights, above all never realizing that, though the past is the richest of all gifts given to them, it is given only on condition that they learn from it rather than embalm it. Hide this truth from them and we will have won the game.

Of Complacency

In your latest communication you show, if I may so, a singular lack of discernment. May I also remind you that I can at any time discipline you in ways most unpleasant to you while being most pleasant to me. Never forget that it is only in the realms of the Enemy that luxuries such as relationships exist. Among us we have only pragmatic partnerships. The Enemy offers covenants, we can offer only contracts. One of our recent achievements among humans is that we have succeeded in shifting much of their thinking from living and working on the basis of covenants to living and working and relating on the basis of contracts. This way we have wonderfully weakened the fabric of their society in both professional life and personal relationships. This is probably among our least publicized successes, which makes it all the more valuable for us in working among them. I digress.

The reason for my displeasure is the great concen you express at the so-called mainline churches being left far behind by both evangelical and fundamentalist churches. To be alarmed at this shows that your judgement is impaired. What you should be alarmed about is something very different. The success of these churches, far from being a threat to the church for which you are responsible, is actually a potential resource for your church, did its people but realize this. Therefore, the evangelical and fundamentalist churches are a potential threat to your efforts to weaken this Anglican or Episcopal church of yours. Mind you, I am not saying that this threat will become a reality unless you in your stupidity allow it to.

Let me explain what I mean, while there is yet time and before you do any more well-meaning harm. Do not try to show these Anglicans the immense success of other churches. They might then begin to ask the reasons for this success. Instead you must inculcate in them a hearty contempt for all that goes on in other places. Emphasize the vulgar enthusiasm of their worship, the rabid anti-intellectualism, the laughable style and content of their sermons. Encourage these attitudes as much as you can.

But, I can hear you say, is not this playing into the Enemy's hands? Is not this to preserve the integrity and cohesion and self-esteem of this Anglican church? You must look beyond the obvious. There is something of much more significance at stake here. In the present apocalyptic period the human spirit has some very pressing needs. On every side is immense change, threat, insecurity, questioning. The evangelical and fundamentalist churches realize this. They also know that in the Bible are some rich resources that enable a response to all this uncertainty. They speak to their people incessantly of apocalypse, Armageddon, rapture, end times, the Day of the Lord. That they do this obsessively and manipulatively does not change the danger to us and to our plans that the mainline churches may begin to explore the meaning of these terms. Used responsibly, these terms and the images attached to them can serve to channel joy, hope, and meaning. At present the mainline churches ignore these things, although the very same fears and questioning and anxieties are present in their own pews. In your Anglican church there is an implicitly agreed taboo against mentioning these things. To do so is to be considered unsophisticated — the ultimate condemnation.

Do you begin to see why we need to prevent your Anglicans from suspecting that these other churches might have lessons for them? Do you begin to see the wisdom for us in making sure that Anglican church life studiously avoids questions about judgement and the end of time? To do so is to ensure that it will go on failing to meet some of the needs of its people as they grapple with the turmoil and stress of the age. This is exactly what you want to bring about to achieve your objectives. Once you allow these Anglicans to study and reflect upon these things intelligently and creatively, you play straight into the hands of the Enemy.

Let me mention another related mistake made by the mainline Christian churches. Particularly in recent centuries, Protestant mainline churches have assumed in their people a high degree of education and sophistication. This is particularly true of Anglicans. Many of their clergy look out on Sunday at men and women, many of whom are professionals of some kind, and assume that these people are knowledgeable in their faith. They forget — and it is very much in our Master's interest and in your own interest that they should continue to forget — that in an age when there is a great gulf between faith and culture, it is perfectly possible for a man or woman to be highly cultured, well educated, and extremely sophisticated, while at the same time being a child in the Christian faith. Such people need to be addressed as beginning learners. As long as agents such as you keep this insight hidden from the clergy, you will go a long way to ensuring that much mainline preaching remains ineffective

I have to say that you have not shown yourself in a good light in these matters. There is such a thing as becoming too clever. Ironically this is what mainline churches tend to do. They look at the methods and approaches of evangelical and fundamentalist churches, and they are not attracted to what they see and hear. But they make the mistake of dismissing the motivations and the objectives behind the methods. Such motivations, among them a concern for individuals, a commitment to the importance of scripture, a recognition that the gulf between culture and faith calls for a new — yet very old — way of communicating Christian faith, are absolutely necessary in any Christian enterprise worth the name. Keep these things hidden from your clients and all will be well — for us and for our Master.

Of Overconfidence

Reading your recent reports makes me rather proud to have been your trainer and mentor. One of the joys of these lower regions is that pride is not a sin, as it is above. I can indulge to my heart's content. But I digress.

So far, I feel justified in my choice of you for working with this church. You showed an admirable greed in your response to my last letter. You asked for a promotion. Apparently you feel that your results in recent years make the further weakening of this church inevitable. I shuddered when I read the word *inevitable*. If you value your position as a tempter in the field, you must remember that nothing, absolutely nothing, can be regarded as inevitable when you are dealing with the Enemy.

Must you be reminded again of what is on the very first page of the training manuals? Have you so easily forgotten how the Master had triumphed when the Enemy's son was actually in the grave, utterly and completely lifeless, his method of execution ensuring him the utter contempt of all who witnessed it or heard of it? The pathetic dregs of humanity he had gathered around him had been scattered to the four winds. I can recall so well the crash of that great stone rolling into place at the mouth of the tomb. The echo of it rang through our underworld as a great shout of triumph. Even more, the Enemy's son came to the very borders of our domain. We watched him wandering lifeless among the unnumbered dead in that ghastly prison house between the worlds. I realize now that we should have seen the danger of his reaching out to others even in his own near helplessness, but we were lulled into complacency by our sense of triumph.

All of this you must know by heart. Every page of it was drummed into you in training. You also know the ghastly sequel — the sudden intervention of the Enemy that sent us reeling back, the shattering of the rock, the use of incalculable forces at the heart of creation — and in a moment all was lost of that great and hard-won victory for which we had toiled for millennia.

Forget these things and you are useless to the cause. You will be destroyed before you know it, blasted out of existence by those same forces, which are older even than our Master himself. I recall the many times when inexperience in the methods of the Enemy has proved fatal for agents such as you. Some two and a half of their centuries ago I had assigned a brilliant agent to work in the Church of England. He had realized great success. He had brought the whole damned church — how I wish that word described a fact rather than a wish — to its lowest level for many years. We were about to celebrate a rare victory. The Enemy was desperate, yet he still managed to pull off a subterfuge so old that we should have been prepared for it. He engineered the birth of a sickly child in a large family. It had not even occurred to our agent to check the Wesley family. Even into adulthood there seemed little to threaten us in the activities of this measly son named John. Then one ghastly evening down some backstreet in London, the Enemy managed to grab him beyond all our efforts to get him back. This most unpromising of moles was activated and, before we knew it, most of the achievements of the previous half century were undone. Let this be your warning that nothing — do you understand? nothing! — can be taken for granted when you are dealing with the Enemy against whom we struggle.

Come to think of it, another classic example is to hand as I write. I notice that your request for a promotion includes your wish to be sent to the South African sector. You feel that the racial tension there would be fertile ground for your particular gifts. You show a disturbing unawareness of recent changes there that have caused us great disappointment.

Again we were caught on the wrong foot by the Enemy. After our success in the formation of the apartheid policies, the polarization of forces in the country, the wonderful rise in torture and killing on both sides, we were fully expecting to win at least a battle in our eternal struggle. We had watched very carefully for the coming of any figure who might interfere with our plans. Reports on every known public figure flowed in.

Once again the Enemy made us into fools by hiding his agent in prison for half the fellow's lifetime. Then, when everything seemed ready for political and social disintegration, he managed to get the authorities on his side. We had always thought we had them securely in our claws. But in the end the Enemy got to them and turned them. The government freed Mandela, the agent the Enemy had been preparing behind prison walls, and all our work was undone. Mind you, we still have hopes for South Africa. With all those painful memories, simmering hatreds, endless class and racial resentment, we may yet see some good things happen for our cause. We have some good agents stirring the pot.

Now if by chance I have whetted your appetite even more for a posting there, the fact remains that you cannot have it. I realize a North American posting may not seem exotic. In some areas its winters are particularly hard on us, considering our native temperatures. However, here is where you remain, at least for the present. Back to work.

Of Church Resilience

Reading again some of your past communications to me, I see patterns in your work that are disturbing. You don't seem to realize the immensity and the difficulty of the responsibilities you have been given. Let me repeat what I said to you on that long-ago day that we last met on the borderlands of the Great Fire, when you were setting out on your mission. I recall — and believe me I recall with great precision — I said to you that your mission was nothing less than the weakening of this church to which our Master, on my advice, has assigned you. I realize now that your successes — and I have never denied that you have had these — have been limited by your illusion that the church can be damaged without great effort and much intelligent planning.

What has deceived you is that the church always seems vulnerable. It has been made to reflect the vulnerability of the Enemy's son, which he assumed when he entered the world of humans. To this day we have never fully understood why he did this in the way he did. What he could have achieved by bringing to bear his incalculable power goes beyond all calculation. However, that story will never be told.

To say that the church is vulnerable is not to say that the church is weak. This you must grasp. Many before you in our work have come to grief because they failed to understand this. There is the damnedest strength in this so-called vulnerability. We see this even in humans who follow him. They will be so vulnerable in so many ways that they make us laugh. They will even confess it to him in their prayers, snivelling their way into his presence. But the very fact that they confess allows the Enemy to inject a kind of resilience into them that resists our best efforts. He and they call this "grace." We have long since learned not to laugh when he gives it to someone we are pursuing.

Forgive my digression about these humans. However, the same is true of this church. Consider how it has come through the centuries in spite of our best efforts. In the early years we attacked it head-on. To this day I can remember sitting unseen in the Coliseum listening to the Christians' pathetic speeches and prayers — they called it witnessing — before the lions entered. I thought it only a matter of time before the movement would be a footnote in human history books. All we achieved was a flood of conversions.

We then tried invasion. The delicious irony was that many of the invaders — in spite of the epithets thrown at them — Huns, Vandals, Goths — were themselves already Christian! However, because many of them followed the ideas of one of our cleverly planted moles named Arius, they were regarded by orthodox Christians as nothing less than barbaric.

It was a massive operation involving every one of our agents between the Danube and the far ends of Asia. I recall watching as Alaric rode his horse into Rome. Again I thought it was only a matter of time. To my chagrin the Christians not only tamed

Alaric and the others, but they headed northwest into the Atlantic and formed new communities among the Celts. I thought again that we had them when they began to give all their time to the perfectly useless task of copying the Enemy's words on to endlessly decorated manuscripts. Some of them went blind doing it. Yet, for reasons I can never fathom, these same gospels sent them into a flurry of intense mission that eventually undid much of our work in Europe.

Time went by. I knew we had to be very careful in our next effort. We allowed them to build their cathedrals. I thought it would divert their energies from things spiritual. I recall being terribly tempted to interfere with the calculations of the master mason as he planned the main arch in Chartres. I felt that to bring it down might be a stroke of genius. It would certainly have been satisfying, but something held me back. I suspect now it was the Enemy infiltrating my thoughts.

As their Middle Ages progressed, we thought of a better way. We would let them get powerful. Even these humans themselves know that power always corrupts. Fortunately, they continually forget it. By their twelfth century we had their so-called Christendom reeking with violence, treachery, cruelty, and hypocrisy. Our hopes were high. Then, without warning, one of our promising recruits — a rich decadent youth for whom we had great plans — converted to the Enemy. His name was Francis. Again we were thwarted. That little animal had the effrontery to laugh in the Master's face.

We persisted. In the sixteenth and seventeenth centuries we tried — and succeeded — in setting them at each other's throats. In the eighteenth we tried tempting them to intellectualism. We laughed when we heard them call it the

Enlightenment. It has turned out to be our best gambit. Of itself it did not succeed, but as I have said to you, it still works its influence among them today, especially in what they call their West.

But once again the Enemy produced resources that undid our work, sometimes the most unlikely resources. Can you tell me what John Wesley and John Henry Newman had in common beyond the capacity to talk interminably? Yet they gave this church back its life in their different ways, in spite of itself. This is what rankles most, that they did it in spite of the church of the time.

I can feel the frustration even as I describe all this to you — victory so often in sight and then so often snatched away. Must it always be so? I think not. I find myself able to recount all this to you only because there are once again indications that frustration may be ending for us. This is the hope we must never surrender. I will write more to you of these matters.

Of Postmodernity

I decided to end my recital of our struggle against this church at a moment of its seeming recovery. What these humans call their nineteenth century was a time when the Enemy seemed to be ascendant in the life of the church. I have often suspected that its poor response to all that he gave it at that time must have disappointed him. A bare century later, this same church is reduced to stubborn survival rather than confident strength. I flatter myself that our policies, and your own hard work, have not entirely been without fruit in the intervening years.

Following their Second World War, the Master decided as part of a grand strategy to give the church in North America the most dangerous gifts of all — acceptance, popularity, success. Their now elderly people still recall those times fondly — the crowds, the full coffers, the endless planning and building, the proliferation of busyness, the accolades of society. We had to be very careful that they did not listen to certain voices. Neibhur and Bonhoeffer were threats to the complacency we were cultivating, but we managed to muffle their voices reasonably well.

Then in the mid-sixties we struck with every weapon we had — massive social change, generational upheaval, an Asian war, civil strife, the lot. We achieved a great deal, make no mistake. We smashed their comfortable ecclesiastical party, undermined every article of faith, decimated their attendance, marginalized their priesthood and preaching, persuaded many that sacraments were superstition and prayer a psychological crutch for the immature. To this day I am proud of that campaign, as you should be, too. Yet here we are at the end of this same century, on the edge of a new one, still battling this church's depleted defences. The best we can claim is that we have weakened them. Do you realize now why I adjure you not to underestimate these Christians? We have attacked, subverted, deceived, tempted them for two millennia, and still they persevere. Do you understand why I warn you against complacency?

Yet, this is not my primary reason for writing. On this occasion I write to tell you something that will surprise and encourage you. Believe it or not, I think there is reason for us to hope, even as they prepare for the third millennium. I am convinced that we now possess weapons immeasurably stronger than we have ever had. We are forcing them to defend themselves on many fronts. This time our weapons are so subtle that most people do not yet realize their existence. We are attacking them from a position far out in the surrounding culture. Out there we have affected their thinking at its very roots. They do not realize that our real target is their Christian faith and all its churches.

We have arranged for their intellectuals to maintain that there is no such thing as truth in anything but a purely subjective sense. It then follows naturally that the Christian faith becomes one of a thousand stories or scenarios, available for anyone to choose who wishes, for reasons known only to themselves. Beside this achievement, as I have already observed, we have persuaded them to hold the rights of the individual above every other claim. Some even believe that there are no rights other than those of the individual. It follows that any institutional action or statement that seeks in any way to question, to discipline, or limit individual action and thought is instantly dismissed as repressive.

You and I can already see this being played out in the life of their churches. Let the church make a decision even in the highest levels of its collegiality, and some cry that they have been robbed of their right to participate personally in the decision. Let the church plead for time to wrestle theologically with the most searing issues of their biological and psychological formation, and some cry that they have been deprived of their right to self-expression. Let the church attempt a theological critique of the political bodies of the country on the basis of scriptural values, and some condemn it as treason.

You can see that these cultural assumptions, now being absorbed by a new generation in an educational system where these things are taken as self-evident truths, can in our hands become weapons to discredit both faith and church. Already we have them listening solemnly in their churches to passages of scripture that speak of the church being the body of Christ, without their having the slightest realization that this collides head-on with the philosophical assumptions of the society in which they live and work.

You can see by now why I write with such relish. In no way do you and I need to be seen attacking their faith or their church. Instead we are quietly removing — some would say we have already removed — the foundation on which both church and faith stand.

I have no doubt that for a long time there will be entities in their culture named Christian faith and the Christian church. Whether those labels will be attached to realities that in any way resemble the originals is the question. Like brilliant art thieves, you and I are not only stealing great art. We are also leaving in its place imitations so well executed that the life of the gallery goes on oblivious to what has happened. I can take you even further into the intellectual wonders we have brought about in their — as they call it — postmodern world. Even if a great art critic were to enter the gallery and reveal the fraud we have perpetrated, the reply would be that, since there is no longer any hierarchy of values by which to measure art, it matters not a whit that the original has been taken and an imitation substituted. After all, appearance, image, and how people-feel-about-it have become everything!

Can you not sense my delight in every word of this! Carry on the work.

Of Spirituality

Once again I want to help you look through a wider lens to see the context of the mostly excellent work you have been doing. It is most important to realize that human beings — all of them, not just these Christians — are in a very vulnerable state. Put quite simply, they are in a chapter of their history where vast changes are taking place. So many and varied are these changes that all their experience is ruled by change — tremendous, universal, implacable.

Such times are familiar to you and me, because, being eternal creatures, we remember many of them. For us, ages such as the fifth century of their era seem only yesterday, but to these people with their pathetically fleeting life span, these periods seem long ago. Moreover, our work in recent decades has ensured that, even if they are aware of such past ages, they regard them as totally irrelevant. We have them convinced that their own period of change is quite unique. This is a recurring and amusing form of human arrogance. However, it serves us well, because it encourages them to believe that little or nothing of the past applies to their present situation. One of their thinkers whom I have mentioned before, a man named Reinhold Niebhur — a servant of the Enemy — tried to draw their attention to the dangers inherent in this attitude toward the past. He was given to saying that every age is under the illusion that it does not have illusions because it has discovered the illusions of its predecessors. Fortunately we have made sure that he has not been heard by many.

The particular transition they are now going through involves the passing of particular assumptions they have held since the late seventeenth century. At that time you and I were able to turn to our advantage a great gift given to them by the Enemy. He revealed to them a new way of thinking about Creation. They learned to use their rational and analytical capacities to open new vistas of knowledge, which they then applied in myriad ways to effect change in their world, and consequently in themselves. We were alarmed at the abilities the Enemy was releasing in them. For a short while it seemed as if he would at last succeed in making them genuine stewards of his creation. He has never given up hope for this plan, in spite of endless disappointment with their performance.

You and I and many other agents can feel very satisfied that we have succeeded in thwarting the purposes of the Enemy. We have managed to take the knowledge he gave them and to twist their use of it in such ways that they are now paying an incalculable price for many things they have done. They find themselves in a world where they are very unhappy, to say the least, and their unhappiness motivates them to discover where they went wrong. As always, the Enemy is assisting them in their search. This is very ironic, considering that in recent centuries, and even more in recent decades, his very existence has become doubtful to millions of them. But he goes on helping them, so much that they are now beginning to think and talk about something very dangerous for our purposes.

They seem to be realizing that the twin pillars of materialism and rationalism, on which they have based their culture's life for more than two centuries, are no longer capable — if they ever were — of responding to the needs of their full humanity. As a result they are beginning to suspect that they have lost something in these centuries. You will realize the measure of the threat to our work when I tell you that an ever increasing number of their voices is defining the missing element as spirituality! So widespread and prevalent is this spiritual questing — as some call it — that it is now showing up almost everywhere, not least in their physical and life sciences.

Human nature and human consciousness being what they are, some of these varieties of spirituality are quite eccentric. Some show signs of being self-centred and neurotic, some even psychotic. Perhaps most amusing of all — much of what they think is new and unprecedented in this flood of spirituality is in fact incredibly old and absolutely familiar to you and to me. Nevertheless, in spite of its lunatic fringe, the newly returning spirituality is powerful and widespread, and it represents, I would suggest, a threat to our work of undermining the church.

I realize that this will puzzle you. As we both know, the present tide of spirituality seems totally uninterested in any institutional form of religion. However, if we are not watchful, this tide of spirituality may affect the life of the church. The danger we face is that the church might seriously take to heart the various forms of contemporary spirituality, discerning the timeless needs and hungers they express in the human mind and heart, and might then devise ways in which to respond to those needs.

To this point, I am delighted to tell you that there is little or no sign of this happening. We have brought it about that the church has a number of responses to today's spiritual hunger, most of them at best nervous and at worst dismissive.

In your report you tell me that some Christians actually ascribe the term "new age" to us demons. We should feel flattered! You also mention that some Christians use the term angrily to condemn anything new they do not understand. How amusing that they are completely ignorant that the last time the Master had to contend with a serious outbreak of New Age thinking, it was among these very Christians. Their movement was then in its infancy, and it was none other than they who were preaching the advent of a new age in the person of their Jesus Christ. It never seems to occur to them to claim his name again as precursor of a new age. I suspect the reason is that we have so weakened them that they simply do not have the energy. If this be true, then we can indeed congratulate ourselves, not so much on any particular skirmish won, but rather on our having drained them of the ability to stay in the field.

I am hopeful. However, because I know the Enemy of old, my hope is careful and tentative.

Of Church Role

I am disappointed in your latest report. Quite obviously you fail to see the threat to our work in this return of a spiritual element into Western consciousness. If this were to deepen and mature — of which there is still little sign — it would be of far greater concern to us than any perceived strengthening of the life of the institutional churches as we know them.

My saying this may surprise you. Perhaps the time has come to share with you what may be the Master's best kept secret. A few of us at senior levels have observed that he does to some extent ensure the continued existence of the church. He is careful to give the impression of attacking it relentlessly, but some of us perceive that, when he sees any real danger of its being destroyed, he has held back.

I realize that this may come as rather shattering news to you, considering the hard work you have been doing and the risks you have been taking for the cause. Reassure yourself. My sharing this secret with you is a sign that you are being admitted into another level of the Master's service.

The simple fact is that there is a certain value to us in the continued existence of the church, particularly in this Western culture we are working in together. For a long time the existence of the church has given the West the illusion that it has retained a spiritual dimension in its life and culture. In reality the West has used the church as a kind of container for spirituality, to keep the things of the spirit within clearly defined boundaries, isolated and marginalized into the domain of subjective individual experience and institutional cultic practice.

So deeply is this ingrained and so readily is it taken for granted as the natural order of things in the West, that many Christians now unknowingly support us in our efforts to make sure that Christian faith remains imprisoned within the personal domain. When the church does try to apply the principles of prophetic Christian faith to public or corporate or political life, these people loudly protest that "their church" — note the proprietary term — "is meddling in affairs it knows nothing about."

All in the Directorate are amazed that this statement can be repeated so often without challenge. It strikes us as quite obvious that legions of gifted men and women within the church have great competence in any field the church wishes to act in or comment on. Yet this obvious fact does not to occur to people because our hard work has ensured that the very word *church* is normally understood to mean its clergy and rarely its immense lay resources. So long as this falsehood can be maintained, we have little to fear from the church. With a little effort on our part, Western society has been able to congratulate itself self-righteously for retaining religion at its heart in the form of the church, and at the same time the church has remained a convenient means of containing and limiting the application of Christian faith.

Recent events on Earth show us another reason why we must make sure that this situation is perpetuated in the West. In the Eastern part of Europe and beyond, where we successfully planted the seeds of Marxism a number of decades ago, we made the mistake of arranging for the society to name the church as its enemy and regard Christian faith as a seductive mirage. We caused churches to be closed, limited the recruiting and formation of clergy, and encouraged a program of education that sought to eradicate all memory of Christian faith.

We have learned painfully the flaws in this approach. At the moment we can only watch as the Enemy's forces rise in Eastern Europe with renewed vitality. We are already finding ways to corrupt this revival of Christian church life, in some areas by poisoning it with ethnic hatred and tribal rage. However, we have a suspicion that eventually an even more effective policy will be to ensure that the Eastern church receives the same degree of acceptance, comfort, and affluence as the church in the West. My own estimate is that within a generation all memory of the church's role in the quest for freedom and social reformation in these societies will be erased or at least discredited, and we will soon have Eastern Christians protesting just as loudly as in the West against any public role for Christian faith.

By all means attack the church. Carry out a kind of guerilla campaign, weakening it here and there, draining it of energy, touching it every now and then on a painful nerve, reminding it continually of its vulnerability. Do all this, but never destroy it.

Except in rare cases it serves us faithfully — all unknowingly of course — as a substitute for the quest for the kingdom of God to which the Enemy's son calls these people.

PS. As you know, this is a device I rarely indulge in. That I use it now is an indication of the importance of what I am about to write. May I emphasize that I write this in absolute confidence.

In my more paranoid — perhaps merely weary — moments, I sometimes wonder if the Enemy is using us in some way by having us refrain from destroying the church. The reason I say this to you is that I think I discern occasions when certain parts of it — sometimes a group of immensely courageous people, sometimes an individual of great sanctity — will challenge the society around them in remarkable ways, becoming agents for the Enemy's will, often at great personal sacrifice. This will happen in spite of our best efforts to discredit or destroy them. In such moments I find myself indulging in a wild suspicion that in some mysterious way the Enemy's son is somehow within this church.

Naturally, in my better moments I am confident that this suspicion is utterly ridiculous. If I believed it, then I would be admitting that neither our Western nor our Eastern strategies — nor any other strategy we could ever concoct — is capable of ensuring the defeat of the Enemy's will for the church. To admit this would be to admit the inevitability of the Enemy's victory and the final defeat of our cause. This is so unthinkable that I shall make no further comment.

When you write, tell me if any similar thoughts come to your own mind. Naturally I have been unable to share such thoughts with any of my peers in the Directorate, though I have my suspicions that I am not alone.

I repeat, this is written in absolute confidence. Should this be seen by eyes other than yours, my existence ceases. Your own may be grievously threatened if only by association.

Of Spiritual Gifts

You will recall that I was overcome by a certain weariness of the spirit when I last wrote to you. By expressing this in writing I realize that I have made myself vulnerable to you in the event of your wanting to betray me at some future time. It is not inconceivable that ambition may eventually make you wish to replace me in this position. Should any such thought ever enter your mind, I would remind you that even at this early stage I possess information about you and your work that can be far more damaging to you than you can ever be to me. Remember that in the Directorate there are none of the sentimentalities that exist in the domain of the Enemy. Among us there are no relationships other than those based on the temporary intersecting of mutual interests and purposes. You are necessary to my purposes as I am to yours. Let us refrain from pretending otherwise and we shall get along famously.

That being dealt with, let us turn to the subject of gifts, which the Enemy gives unceasingly to his church, especially in times of its testing. Our task is straightforward, but this does not mean its execution is easy. Our task is to ensure, as the church moves through this very difficult period of history, that the more gifts the Enemy gives them, the more we defeat the grace of those same gifts.

We have had many successes, some of which were your own doing. Sometimes we have managed to foster among them the illusion that there is no source of grace beyond their own abilities. Such is their extraordinary gullibility that this is rather simple to do. We were able to make most of their successes during the Enlightenment reinforce this lie. The resulting effects of that secularization have never disappeared, at least in the West. At other times we have succeeded in blinding them to the fact that a gift was given. Where they have received a gift and are aware that they have received it, we have used a very simple device. We have merely made sure that the gift became changed in the receiving. You will find this to be your most satisfying way of dealing with them.

Let me recall some examples for your instruction. Consider a congregation where some are given what they call the gift of tongues. As you know, this gift can be the source of joy and peace. Yet in spite of this we have again and again succeeded in using the gift for our purposes. We have merely contrived that some of those who receive the gift begin to regard the rest of the congregation as having a lesser relationship with the Enemy. Nothing could serve us better. Instead of joy and peace we bring anger, hurt, division.

Consider a congregation where some are given a vision of the injustices and inequalities of their society. This vision gives them the incentive to act for justice and to raise the consciousness of those around them in the congregation. For instance, they may point to servants of the Enemy in the scriptures whose names we have tried to wipe from their memories, names such as Amos the prophet. They may point to the commitment of the Enemy's son to the cause of the poor and the marginalized. You will recall what happened in a congregation you once told me about, when this vision was introduced by some of its people. You were worried at the time, and expressed your concern. Yet you will recall the simple steps we took to isolate such activities in the life of that congregation. We simply made sure that others saw this social concern as politically motivated subversion. Once again we created a satisfying brew of anger, hurt, divisions. Those who had received the vision of justice lost heart and left. The majority were wonderfully confirmed in their complacency. You and I can look forward to encounters with many of them.

Again, you will recall that the Enemy's gift of the exchanging of the Peace in worship was recently returned to them. I have seldom seen our Master so disturbed. I myself shuddered. After all, we know that the Enemy's son used the exchange of the Peace with devastating spiritual power. His very touch healed. After he had thwarted death itself he invited his friends to touch him. His first salutation to them after rising from the dead was this gift of peace given with touch. To give Christians this gift again at a time of great fear and fragility was the kind of stroke of genius we have learned to fear and respect in the Enemy. No wonder we were appalled. However, we rallied. You recall what we did. We subtly used their social snobberies and their psychological insecurities, presenting the Peace to them as something rather vulgar, common, naive, childish, at worst even sexual in its implications. So in many congregations what could forge a strong bond of spiritual unity became a cause of deep resentment and division.

The pattern of success is clear. The Enemy gives the gift. We use human nature to twist and cheapen the gift. The Enemy gives back to them the gift of Bible study. We try to sow the seeds of a fundamentalist understanding of scripture, a wonderful source of division. The enemy gives the gift of contemporary music and song. We make sure that many see the new as the enemy of the old.

Never must we allow them to see the gifts of the Enemy as neither new nor old but as timeless and holy. Never must we allow them to see that the Enemy's gifts are given not to satisfy individual taste but for the corporate good, to be shared as in a family, to be received gratefully — tested, tried, adapted, until a way is found for the gift to enrich the whole body. Hide these things from them when a gift is first received. The gift may be offered in a form that not all of them can at first receive comfortably. For some it may be too potent, for others too challenging, for others too new, for some even frightening. It is our task to ensure that things never move far beyond this stage. If we let these Christians realize that it takes time to receive the powerful spiritual gifts of the Enemy, time to understand them, time to respond fittingly, time to rise to the demands of the gift — much is lost for our cause. Before they stumble on these truths, we must inject the poison of mutual mistrust mingled with fear of the unfamiliar. Our great good fortune is that they are pathetically susceptible to such poisons.

Of Media

Reading your report of the great things you have done for our cause by your manipulation of the media makes me feel my great age. The simple fact is that when I was an agent in the field many millennia ago this media phenomenon did not exist.

You tell me that by causing the media to give endless publicity to a particular priest, you have managed to have a mountain of scorn heaped on the church. For that, my heartiest congratulations. It matters not a whit that you had to take great care to present the priest as a saint and martyr in order to encourage the media to paint the church in demonic colours. We both know that when this is all over, we can, if we wish, set about finding his personal vulnerabilities. Then we can without much effort use the media to destroy him in turn. Thus we will have both harmed the Enemy's beloved church and at the same time, with luck, captured a soul from him.

It should be easy to keep from these Christians the truth about the media, because Christians attribute to other organizations the same straightforward — should I say naïve? — motives that they themselves bring to things. And the truth about the media is that they know no loyalty except to themselves. Their appetite is omnivorous and insatiable. In their quest for material, they are as savage as a barbarian army and as oblivious to the pain and destruction they cause. Their decision on whether to crucify a man or woman or exalt him or her to the heights depends solely on their calculation of gains to themselves — gains measured in audience or advertising revenues.

Christians insist on preserving the illusion that the invitation to a media interview implies an interest in the facts or the cause or the issue in hand. This, as we well know to our advantage, is utterly mistaken. These Christians are therefore often devastated by the use to which their earnest statements are put. They are often even more demoralized when their passionate letter of protest or self-justification is itself used merely as further fodder for the insatiable media appetite.

This Christian naïveté must be encouraged. Thus the church, already almost entirely marginalized due to our past efforts, will always be made to appear in the media in a way that at best trivializes it and at worst discredits it. I can recall Paul of Tarsus's vivid awareness of all this in their earliest days. In the letters he left behind he is concerned about the need for Christians to care about how the surrounding culture perceives them. Since today the lens of public perception is the media, Paul's warnings are very contemporary. Yet Christians fail to recognize them as contemporary because our past work as agents of the Master has blinded them. They fail to see that, after centuries of dominating the culture and its communications, they are once again a minority within a culture that at best grudgingly accepts them and at worst is their enemy.

Fortunately for our work, we have so hidden from them the reality of their true situation in the culture that they remain highly vulnerable to it. One of the results of this is their fatal innocence when dealing with the media. The last thing we need is for them to realize that the same friendly newspaper that sells them tiny spaces at exorbitant rates to advertise their services in infinitesimally small print, can turn into a ravening beast if some unfortunate in their congregation or administration steps out of line in any way, especially sexually.

When you come to think of it, every profession, even ours, has areas that require almost no effort. As a professional in the service of the Master, you can be assured that, using the media, you can do endless damage to these people with the minimum of effort. All you and I have to do is to keep the truth from them. We have never given up throwing them to the lions. All that has changed is that the roar of the lion is now the ringing of the telephone from the local newspaper, and the eye of the lion is the lens of the television camera.

Of Worship

It is now some decades since you were given charge of the spiritual health of that part of the Enemy's forces known as the Anglican or Episcopal church. Together you and I have waged a long campaign that is now yielding its successes. Your achievements in what is also part of our Master's domain — for you must always remember that the church belongs almost as much to our Master as to the Enemy — have been duly noted. However, this letter conveys special congratulations to you for the success of the plan that began about a quarter of a century ago when, in a burst of inspired darkness, you conceived the idea of introducing and encouraging a variety of worship forms. In some provinces we managed to saddle them with two books, one called alternative, thus ensuring it perpetual secondary status. In one province we failed to prevent them ending up with one healthy *Book of Common Prayer*, but we managed to include in it more than one eucharisitic rite, thus ensuring perpetual tension.

The wonderful irony is that the revitalizing of the liturgy was necessary. Nevertheless, the results of our seizing this oppportunity to undo the Enemy's work has been beyond our wildest expectations. In less than three short decades we have succeeded in draining the life energy of many provinces of the church in futile and ugly arguments. Even more to our advantage, we now and again have managed to make sure that the issue spills over into the secular press, in such a way as to ensure that it is seen as picayune and obsessive. This has provided further proof, for those who wish it, that the affairs of the church are irrelevant to the surrounding society and not worth the concern of serious and intelligent people.

With particular brilliance you have managed to prevent the issue from becoming a healthy debate. This would certainly have been to the advantage of the Enemy, because it would have brought an exciting and creative element into the life of the church. Preventing such a debate has also allowed those who wish to do so to exaggerate the extent of their discontent with contemporary liturgies. This in turn has resulted in the church as a whole being manipulated by its own anxiety not to be seen as dismissive of a relatively small minority. All this has helped us to give the appearance of a church deeply divided, when in truth it has to deal with a small, if dedicated and articulate, rump.

If I may for a moment digress, the ability of this rump to articulate its concerns is attributable mainly to an extremely small number of voices who happen to be prominent in the literary world — without necessarily being prominent in attendance at public worship. Their very entertaining and readable criticisms of contemporary liturgies have been made possible not least by the failure of those composing these liturgies to include the insights of gifted writers and poets.

So far, as you know, we have succeeded in preventing the formation of a company of literary figures in Canada whose very participation in the formation of contemporary liturgy would give it a profile and respect far beyond the church. Until this is done, we can rejoice that the great thunder of the Te Deum, sounding through recent centuries as "We praise you, O God," now opens with the pathetic and mind numbingly pedestrian phrase "You are God." I am told on good authority that, in the ceaseless worship around the Enemy's throne, which apparently includes various elements of terrestrial liturgy from time to time, this is the one phrase that is forbidden on pain of instant banishment to our Master's domain, no matter how high the exalted rank of the perpetrator!

However, because of your inspired efforts, they now regard the new worship resources not as valuable gifts from the Enemy but as a source of division. As a result we have had to expend only a minimum of our infernal energies on this project. All we have had to do is to use our most reliable and ancient resource — fear, especially fear of change. We simply combine fear and its exact opposite — an uncritical passion for change — mix them together, add judicious amounts of mutual mistrust, insensitivity, suspicion, and the most delicate pinch of paranoia, and hey presto! — we have a most succulent witch's brew. As we both know so well, your enthusiast for change can be just as full of pride and stubbornness as his most conservative opponent.

A word more of congratulation and then a small warning before I end. Your special achievement has been in so engaging the zeal of the church in this issue that it has little energy left over to deal with issues at least as important to its increasingly fragile life. This is my real joy. You have involved them in a wonderfully self-defeating process whereby one side produces endless words to do battle with the words preferred by the other side. Since even the most precise language is incapable of preventing different interpretations, we now have, with any luck, a means of diverting their energies away from essential things, well into what they are calling their third millennium.

As the millennia flash by, you will discover that there is no sweeter satsfaction than helping these humnas to prevent the coming of the Enemy's kingdom, not by their doing evil but by our gently guiding them to the conviction that, even as they successfully block its coming, they are dutifully and tirelessly serving it!

Of Liturgical Change

I have been celebrating your success with some of my other senior colleagues. Perhaps I have been overdoing it. I am open to correction in this as in all matters of the Master's business. Some down here are suggesting that I give you an age-old warning about your work in the fertile field of liturgical change. These colleagues remind me, as I do you, that the Enemy's ability to rescue even the most dire situation should never be underestimated.

Your inexperience leads you to a blind over self-confidence. Those of us who have long and bitter experience know that, in a matter like this, the Enemy may succeed in reminding faithful followers of an ancient truth, which says that the perfect may often become the enemy of the good. He may help them to realize that no liturgical expression can fully reflect the mystery and majesty of the Enemy's power and purposes, which even our own Master acknowledges, albeit grudgingly. Should the Enemy succeed in opening the eyes of these people to these things, then our efforts would quickly be undone. You and I would be revealed and our destructive work shown for what it is. A renewed and united church would sweep away our influence.

Consider the consequences for you if these humans should even begin to recover a sense of being one in the body of the Enemy's son. Consider your fall from our Master's favour if these so easily divided wretches began to regard each other as brothers and sisters in the faith, irrespective of the forms or words they use to express their allegiance. Imagine the effect of their becoming indivisibly united in a search for ways to express their faith in the Enemy to the society around them. Above all, consider the consequences for our cause if these people were to accept the gifts given them by the Enemy, gifts that lie hidden for their finding in the riches of their contemporary litrugical resources.

I can recall the fun I had in what humans call the sixteenth century with a young demon like yourself whom I was training. Then, too, we had infinite hilarity with them as they put each other to the fire and the sword because of the introduction of new books of worship. They directed even greater invective at new books in those days than they do today. I trust you realize that one of those long-ago books is none other than the book some of them regard today as the perfect expression of Chrisian liturgical life. Then, too, so few of them could be brought to see that the new forms, far from being a conspiracy to undermine the church, are in fact a new, if imperfect, instrument for the next stage of the journey to which the Enemy, with inexhaustible and incomprehensible patience, calls these people. What an infinitely precious support to our purposes is the shortness of human memory!

Above all, keep before them the illusion that the different rites are rivals — even more — that they are implacable and bitter enemies. Hide from them the realization, so obvious even to us, that while the older rites are magnificent and timeless expressions of their heritage, the newer rites are courageous — and often beautiful — probes sent out to give renewed expression to those gifts eternally in the giving of the Enemy as resources for the future. As long as we can hide this truth from them, we can have the delicious satisfaction of hearing them preach passionate sermons about the call of Moses to go forward in the wilderness, and at the same time remain quite determined to look resolutely back to a remembered and romanticised Egypt.

Remain vigilant. Always be aware of the possibility that you may fail in this enterprise. I am haunted by the fact that, with all the bitterness and even hatred we were able to engender in the sixteenth and seventeenth centuries, the Enemy still succeeded in making it possible for this same church to achieve a synthesis, and to take to its heart the new things it had so bitterly fought over. It could happen again. Hell forbid!

Of Renewal Movements

I have rarely been so appalled! Perhaps the reports a couple of centuries ago of the Wesleyan revival caused me similar anxiety. Perhaps too the reports from the Great Revival in America. And how I wish I could forget the Anglo-Catholic work among the poor of London in the late nineteenth century, which filled their nostrils with incense and at the same time formed housing societies for them. All of these deeply threatened our work by strengthening this church and other churches.

Everything in your recent reports about the renewal movements they call Cursillo and Alpha tells me that I may be just in time to save us both from an appalling fate. Why can you not see what I immediately see in these movements? Do you recall what I said about the weakness of this Anglican or Episcopal church as an agent of conversion? Their gift is sanctification, the slow, gentle growing and deepening of souls. This is why they are uncomfortable with the very word *evangelism*. But the Enemy realizes this about them, for some mysterious reason accepts their limitations, and decides to achieve his ends in other ways. If the normal life of Anglicanism shuns the direct approach, the Enemy will find another way.

The Alpha and Cursillo movements show all the signs of being his work. Think about what goes on in them. To be with others who affirm you, care for you, surround you in the name of the Enemy. To be invited warmly to align yourself with his forces. To become intentional about the things of Christian faith. Can you not see a threat in all this? They sing the most attractive and invigorating songs. Sometimes they clap and smile and laugh and actually touch one another! Have you the least conception how unlike traditional Anglican behaviour this is? Up until now, most Anglican congregations have tended to look upon such behaviour as they would upon the bubonic plague.

Again, these people sometimes meet in small groups. They actually pray for one another. Can you not see that the Enemy has found a way to introduce into the life of this church the very elements that may enrich and strengthen it? If they put this practice of prayer together with the magnificent liturgy they already have — which hell forbid they should ever do — then our plans for them are scuttled.

We must immediately set out to drive a wedge between these movements and the official church. We can start quite simply, but we must choose our arrows and our targets well. Think of the people we are dealing with. They are largely of the professional class. We must make them feel a little foolish about doing these things I have described. Never mind that the Enemy's son told them that they need to discover the child in themselves before they can even glimpse the kingdom he talked about. They have never really heard this saying, so they will not think of it as a defence against us. Think again. Many of them are middle class, some even upper middle class. These are important things to know. You may think it old-fashioned of me even to use such terms, but the fact is that, as their society becomes more egalitarian on the surface, its underlying class structure becomes more subtle and pervasive.

There are certain words that will work like magic in the subconscious of these people. Come beside some euphoric Anglican soul as he or she is exercising long neglected vocal chords — not to mention hip and arm muscles — in a full throated rendering of "Here I am, Lord." Just in the middle of the third chorus whisper the word *undignified*. Get him or her to imagine for a moment what sophisticated friends would think or say if they could witness this moment. You will be delighted with the results. If you need more ammunition, try the word *sentimental*. Or, with some Anglicans the word *common* is a devastating description of any activity, even though it describes the book they rightly hold dear, the *Book of Common Prayer*.

There are other strategies you can use, if necessary. You might drive a wedge between the clergy and these movements. Suggest to the clergy that the movements are beginning to accomplish what they themselves cannot. Whisper in a few ears that people might be made disloyal to the church by these movements, giving their prime allegiance to the movement. In reality nothing is more unlikely. The real danger to our Master's cause lies in the insistence, certainly of the Cursillo Movement, that the newly affected Christian live out his or her spiritual journey in the life of the church.

By the way, something I very nearly forgot. You might be able to enlist the aid of some church musicians. Not all by any means are prepared to be our allies, but some will join us if we present our campaign as being against vulgar enthusiasms, overemotional liturgies, and above all, bad music.

I have given you some pointers on how to proceed. You must do so with all possible dispatch and determination. Much hangs in the balance. Even at a distance I can smell your fear. Believe me, it is the most pleasant of sensations.

Of Music

I am encouraged by your slyness. It becomes a tempter who has an eye for preferment. Your latest report on the state of music in this church makes wonderful reading. What you have to tell me is so good to hear that I am going to allow myself the rare levity of a pun and tell you that it is music to my ears!

It is perfectly obvious that this whole area is rife with possibilities for devilry of the most enjoyable kind. After the ghastly dangers facing us with the Cursillo and Alpha things, your report came as a glass of pure water to a thirsty soul — something, by the way, that we delight in dangling before our new arrivals here. Their agonies are the highest form of enjoyment we can imagine.

You tell me that there is constant bickering about music in almost every congregation. You tell me that in some congregations where only traditional music is played there are muttered requests for some contemporary music, and that in parishes where contemporary music is offered there are resentful demands for the tradition. You can see how ideal this is for our cause. That nobody can be satisfied is immediately obvious. With little effort on our part, we can continue to make sure that positions become so hardened that music and song, one of the higher gifts given by the Enemy to these humans, can instead be transformed into a source of vicious argument and even personal hatred.

A recent report came to me from a colleague in a neighbouring sector whom I am also directing. He had been working to derail a coming together of three small denominations in the United States. In spite of his best efforts the union went ahead. They had done their work with immense care, much to his frustration. They had constantly prayed about it at all their joint planning meetings. As you know all too well, human beings in prayer are almost impervious to the efforts of all but a very experienced tempter. But, lo and behold, when the merger of the three took place, our agent found such fertile field in the music life of the new denomination that in a recent report he is still optimistic about the weakening and eventual demise of the union. Joy indeed.

The fact of the matter is that many Christians do not realize the power and significance of the gift they have been given in music and song. Many of them see these things as optional addenda to their worship. They rarely realize that music can be the bridge that leads the soul to the Enemy when the more obvious bridge of word, powerful though this be, has proved insufficient. You and I know this because we have often had a soul within our grasp only to be thwarted by a soaring chorale or a simple tuneful chorus.

Obvious as this may be to us tempters, you have discovered for us in recent decades that music offers a rich opportunity for dividing and conquering in Anglicanism. Many Anglicans are quite convinced that souls can be lifted only by music that can be defined as "good." It is almost impossible to get from them a definition of what they mean by the term "good." It is always uttered in a way to suggest that anyone who has to ask for such a definition is already hopelessly outside some undefined pale. They appear to believe that the quality of the music sounding in a soul's ears takes precedence over the soul's arriving at the Enemy's throne.

There is something toward the end of your letter that worries me. You venture the thought that these people can quite easily avoid the trouble we wish to make for them by playing and singing a spectrum of contemporary and traditional music and song in their worship, applying responsible standards to both. This is the kind of statement that worries me about some of your judgements. You sometimes reveal a naïveté about human nature that may yet prove your undoing. This calls for another communication on my part. Meanwhile, keep me up to date on this area of congregational life.

Of Choirs

Every word in your report bears out what I suspected, but I wished you to discover these things for yourself. You feared that our work with this congregation would be undone by their use of a spectrum of music styles in their worship. Now that they have begun to do this, you begin to see why, from our point of view, it is the very best thing that could have happened. I can tell by the tone of your report that you are rather relieved to be reporting some progress.

Because you can sometimes show yourself to be blind and deaf to the reality of these miserable people, I was critical toward the end of my last communication. Experience will refine your methods. Meanwhile I sometimes worry about you. Did you not realize that the congregation that tries to have a spectrum of music is even more open to our schemes of division? Whenever I come across such a congregation I rub my upper claws in anticipation of the most satisfying trouble. Consider the possibilities.

The first thing we bring about is the existence of two choirs. Make sure that each is labelled, and thus limited. Use misleading but well-meaning language such as *traditional* and *contemporary*. Because the so-called traditional choir has been in place for centuries — not the individual members, of course, but the tradition itself — the musicians and singers who express the so-called contemporary can easily be cast as interlopers, even invaders. Without much difficulty the traditional choir can be brought to see the new music group as the Romans once saw the Goths and Vandals.

As soon as this has been achieved — with sufficient intensity and application of your attention — corresponding feelings of enmity can be formed in the so-called contemporary group. In time you will see a delectable tumour of alienation and division glistening at the heart of the congregation's life. At this stage the possibilities for our work are legion. Unless the church plant is very large, you can create endless arguments about space and time for practising. If the two groups practise on the same evening — very useful for our purposes — you can see to it that mutual resentment develops about the sound of the one affecting the pitch and tone of the other.

Another perfect target for our work is the organist and choir director. If the choir director has consented, or has been pressured to consent, to training both choirs, you can bring about endless arguments over how much time he or she is spending with each choir. Again, the allocation of an already stretched music budget provides a good opportunity for stirring up trouble. You can also make sure, if they practise on the same evening and share the same kitchen for their refreshment break, that neither crowd talks to the other except in the most careful and guarded fashion, like armed guards patrolling a disputed frontier between two political regimes. If this is not sufficient, you can cause more strife by fomenting disagreements about last-minute practice time on Sunday morning.

Sunday morning is a particularly rich time for our purposes. All of these people, being creative and sensitive and gifted, are naturally tense and on edge at this time. All you have to do is something very simple, like mixing up the music stands of one group among those of the other. From that moment you have only to step back and enjoy the results.

A warning, however. If it were always as simple as this, there would be no challenge for us. Human beings can surprise a tempter. I have noticed that, when groups begin with prayer, it is a little more difficult for us to bring about confrontations. I have noticed, too, that, if individuals in both groups get to know each other, they can cross the lines that have been successfully drawn. It takes only a little fraternizing between members of the two groups to undo our best efforts at inculcating mistrust, division, and, best of all, hatred.

Above all else, try to prevent the two groups from co-operating in a really fine and joyful act of worship. There is the real risk that they will discover what is perfectly obvious to us but not to them — that they need not be a threat to each other, and that their combined gifts can bring great joy to many hearts. When this happens, it can bring endless satisfaction to those angels that are always hovering around when Christians sing praises of any kind, sophisticated or simple. Nauseating though it be for us, such singing can bring joy to the face of the Enemy himself. Believe it or not, he actually thrills to their pathetic human attempts to echo something of the music around his throne. You and I know well the reason for this. Every piece that these people compose, every note they sing, every chord they play, is the gift of the Enemy to them in the first place. You and I know this, but humans constantly forget it, and this is where they will always be vulnerable to us.

Of Cranmer

I am glad that you found my last letter encouraging. You tell me that you are now developing a strategy for some strong parishes that provide a spectrum of music and worship styles for their people. I await your future reports about this with much relish. When we destroy weak and ailing congregations it gives us satisfaction, but when we bring a large and strong congregation to its knees — other than in the sense the Enemy wishes — then we savour it beyond measure.

I don't think you fully realize the key nature of this activity they call worship. I am convinced that the capacity for song and music is a special gift given by the Enemy to these humans, so much so that I wish to write you a little further about it. Worship is at the heart of the Enemy's plan for these humans. Ironically for you and your responsibilities, it is even more at the heart of this Anglican tradition than of many others.

While the Christian churches that emerged in Europe in what they call their sixteenth century were all formed by a charismatic figure whose main strength was a formidable knowledge of theology, this particular era of Anglican formation was dominated by a poet dramatist! When we look back, we can see that this is what Thomas Cranmer really was. I remember him well. You recall how we managed to make him seem quite ridiculous by having him change his position almost by the day as he saw the fire coming nearer. At the time I thought that we had wholly discredited him, but we discovered later that his almost effortless lyrical prose would live after him. We should have tried to throttle his creativity rather than undermine his courage. In the end we did not succeed in doing either because at the last moment he showed himself — no doubt with the help of the Enemy — to be a person of enormous integrity and courage.

However, I am glad to say that Cranmer's genius serves us today in a quite unexpected way. The wonderful truth for us is that some Anglicans have done to Thomas the very last thing he would have wished. They have embalmed what he wrote, thus ensuring that, for them, the process he so wonderfully began will not continue. Can you not see Thomas at work today if he were alive? He would be a torment to us. We would have to destroy him again to prevent him enriching the church by adapting contemporary liturgical insights from every corner of the world, just as he explored the liturgies of Europe in his own time.

One of the subtle little things from which I take satisfaction is the success of my suggestion to insert into Anglican minds the conviction that the ultimate criterion for liturgy is that it remain unsullied by any stream other than English Christianity, and that it issue from no time earlier than what they call the Reformation. The more you and I succeed in this, the more we will cut them off from the rich variety of those centuries of liturgy that flourished before the Reformation, as well as from the worldwide creativity of their own time. It is easy to make some of these people blind to the fact that the Enemy is being just as profligate in his creativity as he always has been and always will be.

I hope you realize the joke. The fact of the matter is that Thomas is indeed alive, but in the peculiar and inimitable way the Enemy has of making this possible. Within what the Enemy calls the Communion of Saints, Thomas lives in the work of those who now search for an ever new expression of liturgical speech and song. As always they will fail, if only because the language and music of heaven will ever remain beyond human reach. Indeed, Thomas himself would have been the last to claim that he had succeeded in bringing the choirs and speech of heaven to earth. That he did succeed in bequeathing something of immense beauty can never be denied. His work remains the measure of anything they try to do. But we must prevent them from seeing that they need to emulate Cranmer's way of working rather than to preserve his particular expression of Christian prayer and worship eternally beyond change. We also need to prevent them following Thomas in his wonderful capacity to reach across the liturgical worlds of both their past and their present.

This is an area of contemporary Christian life in which we would do well to concentrate our energies. Worship is the well at which they must always drink as they journey through the wilderness of their history. If we can only succeed in making this well bitter, we will slow their journey. Better still, if we can poison the well by mixing in hurt and hatred as they come to drink in their different ways and with their different needs, we may even succeed in halting their journey. What a day of joy that would be for both of us and for the Master. With nothing to slake the thirst of their spirits, we could work our will upon them, slaughtering our way to a victory that would touch the very throne of the Enemy. Sweetest of all, the resources for our victory would be none other than the gifts of praise and prayer that he gave these people in the first place. The very thought of this is intoxicating.

Of Bishops

You tell me that you have been concentrating in recent months on a certain individual, a bishop of this church. You obviously see possibilities of achieving some good things for our cause through this man, but from what you have told me so far, I cannot be sure what will come of this. It is many centuries since I had dealings with a bishop. I am proud to say that a number of them have found their way to our Master's domain through my work. I am particularly proud of capturing a bishop named Wolsey in that period when I was in the field, before I became a supervisor.

Actually, we have a lot of bishops down here from certain periods of history. We have a good crop from the eighteenth century. There are rather few from this century, and if you can get one, it will be a feather in your cap. I think, however, that it will not be easy. Power, as you know, is the factor that corrupts. The modern bishop has been so shorn of any real authority that we can no longer entertain any great hope for power as a source of temptation. I think the best bet these days is to try to destroy the person's spirit by less glamorous means. Let me explain.

The church has never been so ambivalent about hierarchy than it is today. Anglicanism enjoys ecclesiastical order as a comforting echo of things past but does not want hierarchy itself. The last thing it wishes for is a bishop to be actually powerful. Rather it wants the appearance of strong hierarchy. Its most determined effort to bring this appearance into being is the service of — mark the word — *enthronement*. I once heard a wise bishop remark that there were people in his diocese who wished him to give directives, so that they could then ask who in hell did he think he was! I name him as a wise man because he has seen into the heart of their dilemma.

The bishop's being regarded as embodying power but possessing none offers rich opportunities for our Master's work. Today massive expectations are placed upon the bishop. (Incidentally, since comparatively few women have been elected bishop, we have yet to see clearly what insights and methodologies they will bring to the job.) At present we have only to look at the job descriptions produced before any episcopal election to see opportunities for our cause. One has only to read them to lick one's lips in anticipation of the certain failure of any human being to fulfil such expectations. The Master has given strict instructions to any of us involved in this area of the church's life to make absolutely sure that these utterly unrealistic expectations continue to be as inflated as possible.

The quest for the perfect bishop is like the mediaeval quest for the unicorn, made possible only because people believed that a life form of such perfect proportion and purity actually existed. By our perpetuating among Anglicans the belief that there exists a being who possesses the combined qualities of archangel, philosopher, chief executive, and saint, we will be able to ensure that they will never cease to search for this being.

Since, as we both know, such a being does not exist, we know that these people will again and again discover that they have elected a thoroughly normal and all too obviously human being! Each time they make this discovery their wrath will wax great and will continue to be directed at the bishop in both conscious and unconscious ways. Even as I write this, I exult in the trap we have so easily set for them and into which they invariably stumble.

May I add — a small but important victory we have brought about in recent years is the death of the concept of the bishop as father in God. There was a time when he and the clergy lived in this kind of relationship, and clergy went naturally to their bishop with concerns. The irony is that, given the kind of society they live in, clergy need this relationship even more than in the past. However, thanks to our work, the more they need it the less available it becomes. Even to write this gives me satisfaction.

In our work with the church we have learned that direct attacks on institutions and traditions are sometimes not as effective as letting the form endure without the reality. By being seen to attack something, we run the risk of uniting people in its defence. By leaving the outer form and emptying it of substance, we puzzle and confuse people, creating a most gratifying anger and disunity. To do this is your vocation.

However, I must issue another warning. A new generation of bishops, both men and women, is appearing who move through archaisms like enthronement but are not one whit impressed or deceived by them. They know the present-day realities of their function and office. Status today has to be earned rather than merely donned with a garment. Simplicity and servanthood are the surest way to effective oversight. The preservation of their own inner being and their own dearest relationships is primary if they are to be good servants of the Enemy. True success lies not in their striving to be the source of all wisdom and leadership, but in releasing the varied gifts of their people both lay and ordained. Be warned. When you encounter such a person who has just been elected to episcopal office, I suggest you prepare yourself for some very hard work in your efforts to destroy them.

Of Ordination of Women

I wish to develop what was only a passing thought in one of my previous letters. You will recall that we were on the subject of divisions among the churches of the Enemy. This has always distressed him. When he sent his son to become human, and when the son had formed the earliest community of followers, he paid particular attention to this matter of unity. The son's desperate appeal to them to remain united is recorded in the scriptures. They regularly and unctuously read it while perpetuating their divisions.

But we have perfected endless ways of reinventing their divisions. Once upon a time they railed against each other over what they called theology. Today theology is no longer fashionable. In the culture at large the very word has become transformed into a sneering title for any thinking that is seen to be disconnected from reality.

At another stage in their history they used to go at each other's throats over forms of worship. Anglicanism is particularly rich ground for this. For a century or so we profited hugely from their determination to divide themselves into angry competing herds of High and Low churchmen. This division, too, has become largely irrelevant since the Enemy moved them to begin what they call the Liturgical Movement. But, as you know, we never run out of options. We have now got them more thoroughly divided than ever on issues they were not even thinking about half a century ago. I do not think it impossible that they will soon have armies of zealots piling faggots around stakes on the issue of inclusive language! As I mention this, you should know that I may yet ask you for a report on this subject. For now we will let it be.

We have already chatted about your own successes in the field of liturgy. As I have told you, your suggestion of creating more than one eucharistic rite was a stroke of genius. But there is more. I can remember that when you first suggested the ordination of women I was cool to the idea. I could see endless possibilities in this for the Enemy. Under his guiding, the other half of the human race would be bringing its gifts to ministry. Even now, after a mere few decades have passed, the ministry of ordained women has already shown some rich potential for the Enemy's purposes. I take no little satisfaction in reminding you of my warnings, which you then brushed aside. However, you can be at ease a little. As I have watched the deepening and strengthening of women's ministry, my fears have given way to an acknowledgement that this can, as you first suggested, be of use to us. I will admit that there was, after all, some wisdom in your suggestion.

I was correct, however, in my fear that ordaining women would bring into play a whole new world of insight and action. Therefore we must continue to watch it very carefully. But we can derive satisfaction from the fact that many in the church refuse to acknowledge the value of ordained women's ministry, and so it has become for us another valuable stress factor in the already overstressed fabric of the church. In spite of the extraordinary quality of the ministry of some of these women, and in spite of the fact that only the most jaundiced and obscurantist in the church can still entertain any real hopes of its demise, there are encouraging indications that we can use the residual grumbling and discontent to drain energy from the church.

It will seem strange to you that I should ever attribute wisdom to the Enemy, especially to that despicable creature, his son, but you will recall that the son reserved his particular anger for those who refuse to acknowledge the work of his Spirit even when they see it in action. We can exploit the continuing controversy over the ordination of women by using this major sin for our purposes. I have high hopes because, no matter how magnificently some women contribute to ordained Christian ministry, no matter to what degree the gifts of the Enemy's Spirit are evident among them, there will be those who obdurately deny their reality. This is the blindness that so enraged the Enemy's son. The more I savour this delicious thought, the more certain I am that your work in this area is only beginning. I have a feeling that there are good things ahead. Press on.

Of Women Clergy

I am not sure that I like the tone in which you write about this ordained woman you are working with at the moment. You tell me that she has been ordained for ten years, that she has been a staff member in two large urban parishes, that she has many gifts. Apparently she has applied for three vacancies where she would have been rector of a parish, but you have had considerable success in wrecking all three applications. In one case you saw to it that two male vestry members who were themselves in unhappy marriages were able to vent their present dislike of all women and thus wreck the female applicant's chances of even being put on a short list. In another parish you knew that the outgoing rector was deeply threatened by women, and you were able to help him poison the atmosphere enough to prevent his people from contemplating having a woman succeed him. I forget at the moment how you effected the third rejection. Suffice it to say that this gifted priest is now not only disappointed and frustrated, but is becoming deeply angry at the church, which she is coming to regard as her enemy.

From the tone of your report I can sense that you expect my approval. You speak with relish of this woman's helpless anger. You tell me that she is a priest of the highest quality and that this makes it all the more satisfying that she can be reduced to this state. Part of me echoes your satisfaction, in that I am pleased when any servant of the Enemy experiences hurt and rejection. One priest destroyed means that we have wounded many other people who looked to that priest for ministry. However, note that I said only part of me is pleased in this case.

I find it very difficult to say in a few sentences what I now want to share with you, but I must try. I strongly suspect that as the third millennium of this pathetic but stubborn Christian faith begins, we tempters are encountering something so massive and significant that even I, with aeons of memory and experience, can speak to you only by hearsay from the Master himself.

While the Enemy is ever active in the history of these humans, there seem to be times when he begins something utterly new on a vast cosmic scale. Down here in the Directorate we are beginning to suspect that the Enemy is once again setting out to achieve something in which our Master once thwarted his purpose. When the Enemy formed these humans male and female, he intended them to discover in their wholeness and mutuality the complete spectrum of gifts and powers that he had prepared for humanity. Even our Master concedes that the Enemy had conceived something magnificent — two embodiments of humanity whose likenesses and differences are so subtly blended and balanced that the Enemy has been able to acknowledge them as nothing less than his companions.

As I said, and as you also know, the Master with a single brilliant stroke, thwarted this plan at its inception. The humans have this story — usually referred to as the fall — in their scriptures. It has taken much faithful effort on the part of demons who have preceded you in the field to twist the story, so as to make them blame their fall entirely on the female. This success has enabled us ever since to divide them and thus to conquer.

If, as our Master suspects, the Enemy is engaged in nothing less than a rescue operation to reintegrate those mysterious aspects of creation that he calls masculinity and femininity, then we must act with great care. Notice what our Master did to damage the first attempt. He did not try to destroy them, merely to pit one against the other. This is precisely what we have always tried to do ever since. In recent decades it has begun to look as if our work is beginning to pay off. I am exceedingly hopeful that we have succeeded in making the mutual attraction between men and women a fatal attraction, making each an intimate enemy for the other.

To sum up. It would seem to me that the ordination of women is only a tiny part of something much greater that the Enemy is preparing. If so, we do indeed need to poison the plan once again. But, as the Enemy's son once said — in the only compliment he ever paid us — we must be as wise as serpents. We do what the Master did. We do everything in our power to set them at each other's throats.

My advice to you then is that, with all possible dispatch, you should remove the obstacles from this woman's advancement. See that her gifts and those of her ordained sisters in ministry become fully recognized in the church. Work to have them placed in key appointments where their influence will be most felt. Thus we will create jealousy and resentment and hatred between the sexes, and thus our eternal purpose of harming the work of the Enemy will prosper, not to mention our damaging his church in the process.

But take care. If these humans ever discover the wholeness that is potential in their mutual sexuality, they may find the path to companionship with the Enemy reopened. Think of the horror this would have for us. These appalling objects might once again walk together with the Enemy in a renewed creation. Do you realize that if, in the lives of these humans, masculinity and femininity were ever fully reconciled, the whole of Creation would be affected? May the Master forbid that they should ever find their way back to Eden.

My directions to you have rarely been as urgent. With all possible speed you are to set about prospering the ministry of this woman and her ordained sisters. Much depends on your succeeding in this matter, including, I would remind you, your own skin, tough and scaly though it may be!

Of Clergy

Your recent letter about the clergy whom you encounter gives me much food for thought. You tell me that, as with everything in this culture, the situation is varied and confused. The morale of some clergy is abysmally low; others show great creativity as they grapple with the many obstacles we put in the way of their work; some show great faithfulness to the Enemy, even in situations of tremendous frustration.

I am particularly interested in one kind that you mention. These particular clergy believe — if I understand you correctly — that without direct experience of the Enemy's Holy Spirit, a human's Christian experience is not valid, and that the goal of all congregational activity is sharing this experience in order to build a Christian community.

I, too, have noticed such clergy, and I have noted some peculiarities about them. They rarely use the word "Christian" without an accompanying adjective — real Christians, true Christians, born again Christians, Bible Christians, Spirit-filled Christians. The implication seems to be that there are unreal Christians, false Christians, spiritless Christians, unbible Christians and, if I may manufacture a term, once-born Christians.

None of this is unexpected. As you and I know well, this is not the first age of the church's life when the experience of the Spirit became the litmus test for judging the validity of Christian faith. In ages of great change and turmoil — apocalyptic ages, as they call them — we manage to take personal experience of the Holy Spirit, itself a perfectly valid means of grace, and persuade them that those who have not had such an experience are not real Christians. In this way we introduce much hurt, misunderstanding, and division. As so often in our work, we achieve our objectives not by introducing any new thing of our own, but by twisting what belongs to the Enemy to our gain and his loss.

I note that in your report that you have been devising strategies to prevent some clergy from having what they deem to be an encounter with the Holy Spirit. I can see reasons for doing this. There is always a risk that the experience will transform and re-energize a person's work and make him or her an even more valuable servant of the Enemy. However, I think the risk is worth taking for the sake of what our cause may gain.

I notice that clergy who are, as they would say, Spirit filled, can often be made critical of the rest of the church. Given some encouragement, their critical attitude to the church can be spread among their congregations until we have a number of communities who continue to assume themselves to be part of the church but in reality have severed themselves from it. You can see immediately that this is to our advantage. Anything that weakens the body of the church and saps its energy is to our advantage. The additional satisfaction for us is that we bring this about in the name of the Enemy's Holy Spirit.

There are, of course, other ways in which we can weaken the church by exploiting the illusions of some clergy. Keep a lookout for those who postulate some past age of the church when Christian faith was pure and the church strong, when liturgy was unsullied by change and scripture free from irresponsible interpretation. Foster in these people a determination to restore the present church to this immaculate state, while at the same time encouraging a hearty contempt for the church in which they have been ordained and to which they have promised loyalty. This is an area that can produce very rich results for our work.

A warning for you. We are speaking only of a minority, sad to say. Many others, you must be aware, are a threat to us. Watch very carefully for those clergy who show a radiant faith even in the face of discouragement, an unflagging energy coupled with a deep love for their people. Watch for clergy who mine the scriptures for grace-giving insights, who are aware that they possess a powerful story in the midst of change and turmoil. Watch for clergy who believe that they actually encounter the Enemy's son when they share bread and wine in his name, and that this encounter takes place no matter how they choose to explain it. Watch for clergy whose whole demeanour and instinct is to include rather than exclude, to understand rather than to condemn. Watch for clergy who believe that the Enemy is the ultimate and timeless reality beyond all cheap certainties, glib answers, and self-centred fantasies.

When you meet such men and women, proceed carefully. You are in the presence of one of the Enemy's warriors. Ironically, you are also in the presence of his Holy Spirit. At such moments you are in considerable danger. Be careful.

Of Sexuality

So you have discovered and become involved with the most explosive issue in the church — any church, for that matter. It is also quite obvious from your report that you are excited almost to the point of salivating. You are quite right. There is so much potential hurt and pain and grief in the issue of sexuality, so much opportunity for us to savage the communities of faith, that for us it constitutes a kind of unholy grail.

There are not many things for which we thank the Enemy, yet how unceasingly we thank him for including sexuality in the formation of these humans. Think of the innumerable magnificent souls, some of them spiritual giants, whom we have tried to capture by various means. Again and again they withstood us until we reached for the one weapon in our armoury to which they are fatally vulnerable. How we relish the delicious prospect of reputations disintegrating, relationships rupturing, whole communities at each other's throats, all because of this strange, mysterious, and powerful energy at the heart of their humanity. It brings them in touch with an ecstasy that can energize and inspire their whole being. It provides the source for much of their art. Yet it can also turn them into something that can walk in darker places than the animals can ever know.

Your report takes us to one of the great mysteries of their sexuality — the longing of one human being for another of like embodiment. What an infinitely rich mine of grief and pain mingled with passion and devotion has been here since they were first formed, and how rich it has been for us, whose joy it is to bring grief and pain. Not the least part of this mystery is the observable fact that the Enemy shows no partiality, either in the distribution of his gifts or in his use of the lives of all men and women for his purposes. Again and again genius emerges from heterosexual and homosexual. Great music, immortal art, philosophy, medicine, literature — in none does the Enemy seem to have a sexual preference when he seeks a human instrument for artistic or intellectual creativity.

For the church, there is a particular irony in this mystery. I am sure you have noticed that the human gifts and graces required by their ordained ministry — sensitivity, gentleness, liturgical presence, intelligence, artistic talent, intuition, creative thinking, a sense of the Numinous or the presence of the Enemy — are often richly present in the homosexual person, though by no means are heterosexual persons without them. As I wrote above, the Enemy seems to have no sexual preference. We can go even further and observe that persons whom humans regard as saintly show as little sexual preference as the Enemy himself.

In spite of all this — or maybe because of all this — how fertile this field has been for our work! To continue this work with the dire effects we have brought about so far, we must always ensure that humans think about sexuality in stereotypical images. We must prevent them thinking in terms of known individuals with whom they work and live, particularly those who are respected colleagues or dear friends. For instance, it is most interesting to see what takes place in a person who has long waxed eloquent against homosexuality or lesbianism when they look into the eyes of their own child, now in adult years, and learn that what they profess to loathe and fear is flesh of their flesh and bone of their bone. In almost all cases these people cease to be our allies as agents of condemnation and hatred. As agents of the Master, you and I have felt intense disappointment when love and acceptance and understanding replace loathing, fear, and rejection.

You tell me that the immediate issue is the ordination of persons living in homosexual relationships. In this area we can create havoc. We can have things both ways. We can weaken and discredit the church by giving the impression that it is out to destroy fine human beings, and at the same time we can destroy the perfectly genuine vocation of some of these human beings because of the hurt and rejection they feel. Even more delightful, by getting them to throw the issue into the public domain of the courts and the media, we give immeasurable satisfaction to those who wish to see the end of all communities of Christian faith. These are some of the great satisfactions in this issue for us.

Ever remember that our ally in every aspect of sexual matters is the media. There is nothing more attractive to a radio station, a newspaper, a television station, or any other of today's means of communication, than to be able to run with the hare and hunt with the hounds in matters of sexuality. Let an ordained man or woman commit some perceived sexual misdemeanour, and the media have a feeding frenzy, even if the human being's life — sometimes family as well — is destroyed in the process. On the other hand, let the church make the slightest effort to claim the right to demand certain behaviours from this same man or woman, and the media is once again trumpeting the church's trampling on the sacred ground of human rights and freedoms.

As in so many things, we have them both coming and going. The amusing part is that there has probably never been an age when human beings were so convinced that they are in charge of their own lives, when in fact the reality is very much otherwise. They show no sign of recognizing that this illusion is our greatest weapon. There is no greater demonic joy than to steer human beings steadily toward the Master's domain, all the time knowing that they are fully convinced that their own hands and feet are firmly on the controls of the vehicle in which we warmly receive them!

Of Bible Study

In your recent report you tell me that Bible study is increasing in the life of these churches. You suggest that we may have to watch it carefully. I certainly agree. We need to watch how it develops, but I hardly think there is yet cause for alarm. The increase in Bible study in your Anglican or Episcopal church is a purely relative thing. There has been hardly any in the past; so it is unlikely that we are facing a major threat in the future.

At one point in the report I found myself reading your description of the content of what they are studying. What I see persuades me that things are far from out of hand. You have wisely noticed that most of their Bible study explores passages that seem to speak to the personal dimensions of their lives — their own needs, concerns, inadequacies, and hopes. Rarely do I see any mention of their studying those books and passages that speak to the corporate and social issues of their day. In a word, most of their so-called study is essentially an exercise in self-therapy. Am I correct in this diagnosis?

I can imagine that you are asking what is wrong with their using the Enemy's scriptures in this way? From our point of view — nothing. From the point of view of the Enemy — a great deal. His hope for them is that they grow and mature beyond their nurturing of the self. Our hope is that they never outgrow a fascination with the self. This is precisely why we should give them every encouragement in this revival of interest in his Bible, especially if all they are going to do is mine it for recipes for successful and happy living!

Admittedly this kind of Bible study could conceivably make it a little more difficult for us to infect them with viruses we like to administer — depression, anxiety, fear, anger, and the like — but this is not really a big loss for us. It can be a great help to us if Christians are so deeply involved in this kind of Bible study that they remain totally oblivious to the sometimes cynical policies of the organization in which they work, the political party for which they vote, or the corporation in which they hold shares or stocks — this plays delightfully into our hands and furthers the Master's cause.

There is another kind of Bible study that attracts them. It appeals to the would-be intellectual. I call it the study of the Bible-as-Something-Else — the Bible as Great Literature, the Bible as History, the Bible as the Basis of Civilization. There is no end to the dazzling array of possibilities here, and the wonderful irony is that they all are fascinating and instructive and perfectly valid. The advantage for us is that well-meaning Christians can spend endless hours in such matters without ever discovering in the Bible the purposes of the Enemy for them.

We tempters need be alarmed at Bible study only if we see that the scriptures are slowly impinging on the thoughts and actions of a person — when that person begins to realize that they are in touch with a mysterious reality greater than themselves, when that person discovers that reading or studying the

Bible is not merely a pleasant religious exercise. The danger signal for our work and the Master's cause comes when, in studying the Bible, a person understands that he or she is being addressed by something Other. You and I know well who the Other is!

It will always be a mystery to me how the Enemy uses this pathetic Bible material. It is nothing but a conglomeration of stories, myths, dreams, songs. The only parts of it that I have ever been able to read with anything approaching interest are its history stories. They reek with the most delectable blood and slaughter, deceit and violence and cruelty. Yet for some reason that we have never been able to fathom, the whole seems somehow to be greater than the sum of the parts. Though my bile rises as I write this, and I most certainly would not wish to be quoted, the damned stuff seems to be alive in some way, almost as if the Enemy is inside it and speaking through it. Reason reassures me that this possibility is utterly idiotic even to contemplate.

To sum up my advice — I doubt that there is reason for alarm. Remain watchful. If you see any of the above signs, bring them to my attention.

Of Preaching

I am amazed at what you report. Surely you cannot be correct in your assessment of the state of preaching in the life of the church. You suggest that it is very low. The trouble is that I am forced to take your assessment on trust because I have not heard a sermon for many centuries. I can recall when we tempters in the field used to perch on the gargoyles of the cathedral in Florence to listen to Savanarola as he described his visions of our Master's realm. His fevered imaginings were so far from the realities of the infernal world that we used to roar with laughter.

I suspect, contrary to much opinion, that the general standard of communicating the Christian faith today is actually better than in previous ages. I assure you that it gives me little pleasure to say this, and later I will be suggesting some steps you can take. But I suspect that the problem for the church — delightful to us — is not the state of today's preaching but the situation in which Christian preaching takes place. This situation is largely due to the good work of yourself and others.

You have seen to it that future preachers are rarely taught by those who themselves preach. Preaching is quite often taught by some frantically busy academic who may be very well qualified in some other theological discipline, but who, through penury or lack of seniority, has accepted the additional chore of teaching homiletics. To train preachers in this way is rather like employing an expert in the mining of marble to instruct artists in sculpturing it. Whenever you come across a situation where preaching is being taught by a preacher, look at it carefully. There may be trouble brewing for our cause.

There are other reasons for the church's delightful problems in communicating. Thanks to our efforts, it has not yet dawned on many Christians that the very nature of communication has changed in recent years. These changes ensure that their traditional buildings and pulpits have become barriers to communication rather than instruments to enable it.

However, I think our finest achievement has been so all-pervading and subtle that they do not realize we have brought it about. We have so deftly moulded cultural assumptions that people no longer expect anything of significance to be said from a Christian pulpit. This achievement is, I think, the basis of any success we have had. Have you noticed that in recent years the terms *preaching* and *sermon* are used in the general culture as sneers, when people want to express what is priggish, hypocritical, and irrelevant?

Given the expectation that the sermon will have no relevance to the world, we have been able to ensure that, even when Christian preaching is well prepared and well executed, and even when it contains worthwhile insight about contemporary life, the humans pay no attention to it. It is wonderfully ironic that there is actually a considerable amount of excellent Christian preaching, but obviously neither you nor most of these people can recognize it even when you hear it. We have brought things to such a satisfying state that preachers are at a huge disadvantage even before they begin.

May I remind you that you can never rest on your laurels. Whatever you may feel about contemporary preaching, do not discount the ability of the Enemy to make a fool of you at any moment. While you may be concentrating on limiting the effectiveness of some highly articulate and glamorous communicator, the Enemy may be using the inarticulate stammerings of some unknown priest to utter a single sentence that may affect a human life and thereby open endless doors for the Enemy's purposes. We tempters face the fact that many of the Enemy's greatest champions were enlisted in his service by some preacher whom we had dismissed as totally ineffective according to our standards. Such is the infinite subtlety and cleverness of the Enemy. Forget this at your peril.

A last thought. There is a delicious irony in my last few sentences. It is perfectly true that the Enemy can use the most appalling preaching to change a life. What we need to do is to twist this truth just slightly and to persuade Christians that, because of the Enemy's ability to use even the most awful preaching for his purposes, therefore the quality of preaching does not matter at all. You would be amazed at the numbers of those whom we have already brought to believe this.

Of Evangelism

I think we should do some work in the area of Anglican or Episcopal evangelism.

For some churches evangelism is their daily business. For the mainline churches, among them your Anglicans, it is a very different matter. Indeed this is precisely why I write to you. I smell some good things for our cause in this area.

I think we have a wonderful dilemma in which we can catch these particular species of Christian. On the one hand they dare not dismiss the call to evangelism. This way lies guilt. On the other hand they dislike the types of evangelism that surround them. Like a person who is desperately anxious to be accepted at a party that they secretly regard as tasteless and boring, Anglicans seek for ways to respond to the demands of evangelism in ways that will not involve them in methods and programs they secretly abhor.

The inducing of miserable guilt because you can't behave in a way you think others want you to behave is simply invaluable for our purposes. When you cannot do what you think is expected of you, you become incapable of doing anything. That in turn demolishes your sense of identity and self-esteem, so that you no longer recognize and appreciate the gifts you do possess. Finally you decide that the fault lies in yourself, that you are not a very admirable person — or church — and that all these others around you are quite correct when they dismiss you with contempt. The process is a delightful recipe for self-destruction, and we can readily use it for our purposes with Anglicans.

Human institutions are very like human individuals. Whatever you do, make certain that Anglicans judge themselves by criteria other than their own. Keep them asking why they cannot produce a succession of Billy Grahams, but never let them wonder why they possess the beauty of George Herbert's poetry, the insights of Evelyn Underhill's mysticism, the integrity of Kenneth Leech's spirituality that binds together contemplation and action, the brilliance of Sally McFague in linking Christian theology with environmental issues, the awe-inspiring resilience to pain of Michael Lapsely in Zimbabwe, the courage of Desmond Tutu in South Africa. If you can bring it about, get them to dismiss all of these. Any pejorative adjective will do — social activist, troublemaker, radical, leftist. (Never use the term *Communist*. You would show yourself to be behind their times, thus committing the greatest of sins in their culture.)

Most Christians are simply incapable of seeing that the gifts of the Enemy have been distributed with such profligacy that not only can no individual have them all, but also no one church can possess them all. What we have managed to do since we divided the church is to give each division the idea that their particular church possesses all spiritual gifts. If it occurs to them that it does not, we send them in hot pursuit of what they do not seem to have, or we simply plant in them the idea that what they are missing is not worth having anyway and may even be sinful!

Consider these Anglicans that you are responsible for in this project. Early in their formation we were frustrated by their being on an island. A predecessor of yours worked hard among them in what they would call the mid- and late sixteenth century. He tried very hard to get them to import into English church life the violence and hatred that were raging on the rest of the continent of Europe. While he did not entirely fail, he did not entirely succeed.

(By the way — a small digression. I hope you have enough subtlety to smile at the last thing I wrote. It is a classically Anglican statement! I must be forming some unconscious sympathies with them. Such transference is always a danger for us who work with these humans. We begin to identify with those whom we are working. I urge you to be most careful that this does not happen. I have wondered from your recent reports if I am detecting an increasing Anglican reasonableness and balance in your thinking. If I am, you would be well advised to rid yourself of this quickly. The last things we need to be inculcating in these people — or to be affected by ourselves — are reason and balance.)

For our purposes we need to inculcate in them passion, anger, indignation, intolerance, resentment, mistrust, and most useful of all, a little paranoia. Our success requires their believing that reason and balance and a sense of proportion are signs of weakness, that somewhere there exists an Anglicanism devoid of the unavoidable ambiguities and questionings of the age, and that such certainty can be found by cutting oneself and one's congregation off from the body of the church and defining oneself as the true and only faithful church.

So often our work for the Master is best done by merely hiding the obvious from these humans. We must hide from them that their gift of sanctification is stronger than their gift of conversion; that their gift is in inviting people to the Christian journey, not glibly promising instant arrival; that their best approach is to encourage questions rather than to insist on neat answers. Do not let them see that their gift to others is in accepting them as they find them and, if the person wishes, offering the gentleness and serenity of their liturgy, their sacraments, their rich use of scripture in worship, their gift of quiet prayer. It is useful if they believe that they should go rushing into highways and byways and compelling people to come in. Even though they seldom try this approach, they imagine that the Enemy requires it of them.

Perhaps they may have to answer to the Enemy one day for not rushing out and compelling others to come in, but then, I have always been intrigued by the fact that the Enemy's son himself, even though he would tell a story about compelling people to come in, rarely, if ever, did it himself.

Have I made myself clear? Your task is to ensure that Anglicans always see themselves through other eyes, and that these eyes, if at all possible, be judgemental. Make sure that they always listen to the statements of others about them, and that these statements are as critical — even contemptuous — as possible. Make sure, too, that Anglicans always accept the criteria and standards of other traditions, even though these may be utterly foreign to their nature and history. Achieve these things and we will see to it that they never see themselves as they really are, and — just as desirable for our purposes — that they never accept with joy and gratitude the vocation the Enemy offers them.

Of Residential Schools

Your reports about the present threats to the church give me the greatest satisfaction and lift my hopes. These threats are all the more satisfying for their not being anticipated by these Anglicans themselves. Even more deliciously, the threats, as we both know, extend to a number of Christian churches. I have it on good authority from other agents in the field that some denominations may be looking ruin in the face. However, your particular responsibility lies with these Anglicans, so we will speak of them at the moment.

I can recall when these people began to colonize in Canada. Their behaviour was the usual mixed bag. Some were out merely for themselves and for what they could make off the backs of anyone they could use. We managed to blind some of them so completely to the humanity of the First People in the land that some regarded and treated them as little more than animals.

But there were always others whom we could not recruit to our plans. People who were prepared to work very hard on behalf of the First People, according them dignity and humanity. What allowed us to thwart the best efforts of these people was to blind them to the cultural assumptions they were making, albeit with the best intentions.

As you well know from your excellent work, the residential schools became our focus of opportunity. The vision — and according to the thinking of the day, it was a well-intentioned vision — was that Native children would be educated in these schools, given the ability to function in the white society, learning the language that would give them entry into a society whose culture was assumed to be superior and ideal.

If I may say so, we moved brilliantly. Very little effort was necessary on our part. We merely twisted everything they did. We brought it about that they did not merely offer English as a language. They dismissed Native languages as primitive and useless. They did not merely offer their own culture as the way to the future. They saw Native culture as something best eradicated. All of this they did with the best intentions. This is the supreme irony — wonderfully satisfying for us, tragic for them.

Our trump card was to make them careless about the teachers they selected. We had on our side the general naiveté about sexuality that existed in those early years of the century. The majority of the teachers were no use for our purposes, decent, conscientious men and women who believed in the children and in the future being offered them. But we found a number of sexual deviants through whom we could work our will. Young people were hurt. At first, of course, there was very little result, but we knew that all we had to do was wait, to let the hurt and fear deepen in their lives as they grew into adulthood.

By itself, even this hurt and fear would not have been sufficient for our attack on the churches. Much work through many other agents had to be done to change many facets of Western culture, not least to develop the concept of the individual being paramount and institutions always being suspected in any encounter between the two. Add to this our success in inculcating in late twentieth-century Western culture a hearty contempt for the motivations and methods of previous generations. All past action has come to be judged through the lens of contemporary political correctness. One result is that, even when the contemporary church expresses its deep abhorrence of past cruelties, even when apologies are offered and reparations made, contemporary society makes no differentiation between the past criminal actions of a few and the present expressions of genuine repentance by leading church voices.

A final ingredient in this wonderful brew — again the work of agents like yourself in other parts of the field — is our manipulation of the legal profession. We have had immense success in diminishing the integrity of many in the profession. We have some of them using people within the Native population with exactly the same unscrupulousness as those they condemn so loudly. In the case of these latter predators we have brought it about that their motivation is not sexual appetite but simple greed, disguised by protestations of professional concern and, among some, a cordial hatred of the church.

You can tell how delighted I am with all this. If we succeed in destroying these churches, we strike at the heart of what the Enemy holds dear. After all, his son died to bring the pathetic thing into being. This is a measure of how much the church must mean to him.

There is more work to be done to ensure we cause maximum harm to the churches through this wonderful opportunity our Master has given us. We must now ensure that attitudes in the churches toward Native people harden. We must bring it about that the victim must become the object of blame. This is not difficult to do. But there is an even more subtle way we can poison relationships between aboriginal and other Christians. The reality is that many Native people are committed Christians, and they share with all other Christians the pain of what is happening. But, as you well know, our Master is well practiced in the art of substituting stereotypes for realities. With comparatively little effort you and our other agents can transform resentment at the claims of some Native people into blaming all Native people for this situation, to see them as determined to destroy the church. Thus we will have — if I may say so, with delicious irony — demonized aboriginal Christians.

Remember that we have an important ally in all this. The government, whose policies brought these schools into being in the first place, seems content to see the church carry as much blame as possible. To encourage this we must work hard in high places. Already our work has brought it about that high levels of government measure the worth of all national institutions, be they medical, educational, or religious, in what we have taught them to call "market values" — a wonderful phrase that succinctly names the death of all values.

You may be surprised at what I consider a real danger to our plans. In this case, I have a scenario that is for us nothing less than nightmare. I see these legal claims draining the life of the church in its outward form — particularly its lands and its buildings. I see much if not all of these being taken, tempting us to celebrate a great victory while, even as we do so, a new and fresh wind of the Enemy's Spirit begins to move among these people, gathering them in new ways — actually ways as old as what they call their New Testament — forcing them to search the scriptures the Enemy has given them, calling them to find new and vibrant expressions of their idiotic faith in him.

On the other hand, among aboriginal Christians I see the possibility of the Enemy bringing into being a whole new relationship between their ancient beliefs and Christian faith. Who knows what will be possible in a future where aboriginal societies are not only free to explore and live out their traditions, but are also free to encounter a Christian faith that is not imposed upon them or dismissive of their ancient spiritual experience.

If you think this is nothing more than the neurotic fear of an older servant of our Master, you may be making a great mistake. On peril of your life, I warn you not to forget how often we have been thwarted by the capacity of the Enemy for rising from what we had so often assumed was death. I warn you to watch this present struggle very carefully.

Of Incarnation

You express a wish to taste what you call the texture of human life. You would like to assume the semblance of one of them for a short period. I hesitate to disappoint you, but I must. To tell you why I must, it is necessary for you to know a major limitation of your being a creature of our Master. For some reason known only to the Enemy, it is extremely difficult for one of us to become one of these human creatures. As I have hinted, it is not an absolute prohibition. Our Master himself can assume human form, and there are rare instances when a few of us at very high levels in his hierarchy have been allowed to do likewise. Even then it is only for very short periods, and to assume the form consumes vast amounts of energy that quickly exhaust us. The limitation is particularly galling in light of the long period in which the Enemy's son assumed human form.

Personally I have a theory about his ability to do this, and our inability to succeed for no more than a few moments. I share this theory with you in confidence, for reasons that will become obvious. I am convinced that he was able to assume humanity only because he was willing to accept the fearful cost of doing so. It is easily forgotten — even these Christians forget it — that he did not merely assume their form. He became one of them. Can you even begin to imagine the cost of that for an eternal being? To become a creature of fleeting time, of physical fragility, of vulnerability to emotions — above all, to have to bow to the darkest of their enemies, death itself.

I feel the need to write to you of this, because I sometimes think that it was neglected in your training. I recall well when the news of the child's birth first descended to us. The details were so preposterous that at first we rejected them as the fevered imaginings of a new agent in the field. We looked at the tiny village, the peasant girl, the pathetically confused would-be husband — he especially caused us much merriment — and concluded that, even if our agent were correct in his suspicion that this was a manoeuvre of the Enemy, then the Enemy had for once miscalculated and underplayed his hand.

In the next thirty years very little occurred to make us change our minds. Even during the last three years of his public involvement, I could see little to be concerned about. A few rural bumpkins trailed after him, at no time showing the slightest comprehension of his thought or intentions. There were moments when I became a trifle concerned that his ability to bring some healing to the human condition might gain him a following, but I could soon see that he did not have the wit to apply his healing powers to anyone who could be of assistance to him politically. Instead he wasted his time healing a motley and marginal lot. It included the mother of one of his friends, the daughter of a minor local official, a few Samaritans, not to mention endless lepers. Not a single one of them was in a position to respond helpfully by using their influence in high places on behalf of the movement he was trying to found.

It was only toward the end that I became suspicious of the seeming simplicity and naïveté of it all. As you will recognize, I would not be writing to you now had I not voiced this suspicion to the Master. Not a day goes by but I give thanks for the intuition that made me ring a warning bell. Had I not done so, I would have disappeared in the fearful purge that swept through every level of the Directorate when the truth of these years was discovered.

It was my idea that we might give him a test. We wanted to find out how he would respond to a contact with real power and influence, the kind of power that would be irresistible to anyone seeking to strengthen a movement. One of our agents was keeping an eye on Nicodemus, a member of their ruling group, the Sanhedrin, and a brilliant and troubled man. We decided to bring them together. Remember that at this stage we still could not believe that this ineffective peasant from Nazareth was even an agent of the Enemy, still less the Enemy himself in human form.

We knew our man Nicodemus intimately in his every habit, weakness, and mood. We arranged that he should encounter the Galilean on a day when Nicodemus was feeling depressed and discontent. We made sure the Nicodemus would overhear some remark about the kingdom of God that the Galilean was for ever talking about. The concept was so imprecise and impractical that to this day I cannot understand how it has continued to affect generation after generation of these people.

They met as we had arranged and, believe it or not, we were totally fooled. The Galilean made no effort to adapt his message to this fellow who could have been an invaluable ally. It seemed to us, as we listened and watched, that Nicodemus was made to feel like a fool by even trying to understand the gibberish of the Galilean about being born again and feeling the wind blow. From the moment the conversation ended, some of my then colleagues — alas no longer with us — suggested that even normal surveillance be withdrawn. Again I give the most fervent thanks that I counselled the continued presence of at least a part-time agent. Because of this I am still here to tell you of these things.

You know the rest of the ghastly story. Having decided that this gentle fool and his pathetic followers were harmless, we let the thing proceed. The Galilean was losing followers because of the increasing demands he was making. Enemies were multiplying; political forces were closing in. We had seen others go this way a thousand times, while we chalked them up as minor victories in our war with the Enemy. The betrayal, the last frantic gathering in the room, the trumped up charges, the sentence, the execution itself. Everything was standard and true to our form. Our agent was so confident that nothing remained in the case that he did not even attend the execution. For this piece of overconfidence he paid most painfully with his life when he was recalled. Had he been there he would have heard the Galilean's extraordinary prayer for forgiveness for those who were at that moment impaling him. This in itself would have alerted us that something very much out of the ordinary was present, and we would have taken action.

We now know all too well that the whole thirty years from beginning to end were a massive exercise in deception. Everything about it was presented to us as its opposite. What we thought was weakness was incalculable strength. What we thought was childish simplicity — the stories, the homely images, the populist style — hid immense profundity. What we considered his vague and unfocused description of a kingdom turned out to be a shining vision that even our best efforts have never succeeded in eradicating from the human heart and imagination. The followers that we had thought ignorant, naive, and dependent turned out to be the shock troops of a movement that has engaged all the forces of hell to this day without our prevailing.

Believe me, all this has been written with more pain and regret and shame than you can imagine. Words like failure and disaster do not do justice to the fatal series of errors made by our forces in that thirty years. On pain of your life, do not forget this recital of mine. We pride ourselves on our gifts of deceit and duplicity. Remember that our best efforts were once shown to be utterly inadequate. Remember well, and never allow yourself to be lulled into overconfidence by the Enemy. Remember that with him all assumed values are turned upside down. Beware of seeming weakness, for it can hide terrible strength. Beware of seeming foolishness, for it can hide the greatest wisdom. Beware of seeming poverty, for it can disguise the riches of the Enemy. Always beware. You know the consequences for failing.

Of Divinity and Humanity

Sometimes your reports evoke a smile as I read them. I find it difficult to define the smile. Perhaps the best word is resignation; however, as I write it, I realize it has a negative tone that I do not mean. Perhaps I should say that your reports sometimes make me smile because I am reminded of my earlier self.

So you have discovered the struggle these Christians are having with their faith in the Enemy's son. (You will by now have noticed that it is a stated policy of the Directorate that he is never to be named.) You think it strange that they are having this struggle, considering that he is the one aspect of the Christian mystery that should be quite clear to them because he became one of them. Is it not the most delightful of paradoxes that after twenty of their centuries they are in a state of crisis and confusion about his identity? This gives me hope for our efforts to rob them of their trust in him.

If nothing else, his coming among them and their brutal response in rejecting him was a shocking lesson for the Enemy. It made him realize, as nothing else would have done, the depth of the inroads we have made into these human beings and their shadowed nature.

To this day we have never been quite clear as to the intentions of the Enemy in carrying through this Incarnation, as humans call it. If by this entry into their human realm the Enemy intended to undo the consequences of the terrible blow our Master dealt them in Eden, he must have been bitterly disappointed. At the time he contented himself with rescuing the son from us. As I and others have told you, we managed after the execution to hold him below for a short while. This is when we became aware of the full power of the Enemy. The Master used every weapon we possessed to hold the son prisoner. When the Enemy came for him I was among the infinity of legions barring the way in battle formation. I have already described to you what took place. I recall infinite light, excruciating pain, utter helplessness, oblivion. When we awoke the Enemy and the son were gone.

The damned thing about it all was that it made these humans aware that we could not ultimately be victorious. This is what the Enemy achieved by rescuing him from the Master's domain. These humans even think sometimes that the Master and his cause had finally been defeated as a result of this unfortunate incident. However, thanks to the resilience of the Master's hatred for the Enemy, we have corrected this illusion in countless terrible ways in their world over the last twenty centuries.

But enough of these dark thoughts. There is also good news in your report. By the way in which you express it, I know that you have missed its significance as good news. You tell me that you have been working hard to get these Christians to concentrate more and more on the humanity of the Enemy's son and to downplay his divinity. The good news is that you have been failing. The very possibility of your succeeding in this makes me shudder. You are utterly mistaken in your efforts, and if you continue in them you will be recalled, with all the frightful consequences this entails. You must do the very opposite of what you have been doing. You must set out to thwart this late twentieth century emphasis on his humanity. We have fought this for centuries, beginning as early as their fourth century. We take credit for the endless representations of him in their arts that show him either as an insipid wraith or an impossibly distanced demigod.

The utterly real humanity of the son is, and always will be, a most dangerous threat to the work of our dark realm. Can you not understand that the whole point of his coming among them was to assure them that no human experience — from the joys and loveliness of life and relationships, to the awfulness of pain and the terror of death itself — would be unknown to the Enemy? Can you not see that in this the Enemy gave them a direct and unbreakable lifeline to himself? He gave them nothing less than a saviour! Now do you understand the threat to our cause? Have you not often wondered why, when a soul was in your grasp, you inexplicably lost it? The reason is that the soul threw itself on what both the Enemy and these humans call *mercy*. The human soul knew that the Enemy would accept it, precisely because he accepted the full humanity of his own son. That, you fool, is why we can never rest!

Because I have had to point these things out to you, the time has come when there is something you must be told. Our telling you marks the end of what I will call your age of innocence as a tempter.

You know that each time you return below after a tour of duty, you walk beneath the great gates which adjure you to abandon hope as you enter. You have never fully realized the meaning of this admonition. Only at a certain stage of maturity is an agent apprised of the darkest secret of this realm.

It is this — *even our Master does not hope for final victory. He knows that in the nature of things victory must belong to the Enemy. We learned this swiftly and clearly when, even with the alliance of death itself, we could not hold the son prisoner!*

You may reasonably ask why we continue the struggle. We continue because for us to exist at all we must live by a hope, even if it is a lesser hope. It shames me to say this, but hope is a need we share with human beings. With us, hate and rage and loathing for the Enemy energize us, and while we know that we cannot destroy the Enemy and his son, we cling to the hope that one day we will be able to wipe all memory of them from human consciousness. You see, our objective is not the Enemy but the relationship between the Enemy and these humans. We can never storm heaven itself, but we may hope to capture the realm of Earth and its human vermin. Perhaps you can begin to see why your recent well-meant efforts to downplay the son's divinity and encourage humans to emphasize his humanity were utterly mistaken. One of the ways we try to lessen the bonds between these people and the Enemy's son is to encourage them to think of him as a distant divinity far above them in Olympian irrelevance.

This letter between us has been no ordinary communication. You now know a deep and dark secret: you and I and all the Master's legions have no final hope. Yet, like me, you will continue the struggle with the Enemy until the Enemy wills its end, as he surely will. What then will be our fate is entirely unknown. Even to write about this fills me with a great sadness.

I find myself thinking the unthinkable. Were the Enemy to come again into these realms of darkness, blinding us with his light and offering an end to the conflict that gives us our very reason for existing, would we be able to bear the unimaginable pain of returning to what we remember as indescribable bliss? Would we be prepared to die, so that we might be born? Even to ask the question brings a chill I have not known since the days before the Fire.

Enough of such weak thinking. The task goes on without flinching, without turning, without even the thought of defeat. I direct you now to return to your work without a moment's delay.

A Final Word to the Reader

When my uncle opened that drawer only to discover these pages, it became possible to publish them as a salutary warning to an unsuspecting church. Only for that happy accident — if anything in the providence of God can be deemed to be an accident — we might have remained oblivious to the reality of an implacable and diabolically clever enemy hell-bent — if you will pardon the expression — on exploiting the weaknesses of the church to bring about at least its diminishment.

Herein is the most important message for the reader. He or she will immediately recall the admonition to the unknown tempter that brings the manuscript to a close. In the command of the Director to "return to your work without a moment's delay" we can see all too plainly that the devilish work continues unceasingly.

It follows therefore that the infinite number of yellowing files that lie in most church offices, studies, and vestries — not to speak of those in synod offices and so-called church headquarters — should be carefully combed for suspicious material. Even as the reader's eyes move over this page, another missive is being placed somewhere for retrieval by one of the Master's agents.

The response of the Christian reader should be to take heed again of the warning of the apostle so aptly quoted, as you will remember, in the final paragraph of my uncle's letter to me: "Be sober, be vigilant; because your adversary the devil, as a roaring lion, walketh about, seeking whom he may devour. Whom resist steadfast in the faith."